Here is your . . .

DESK COPY

. . . of the book
selected for use
in your course.

We appreciate the opportunity
to send you this volume and
believe it will fully meet
your requirements in actual
classroom use.

* * * * * * * * * * * * * * * * * * * *

THE RONALD PRESS COMPANY
15 East 26th St., New York 10, N.Y.

FUNDAMENTALS OF NUMERICAL ANALYSIS

By

AUGUSTUS H. FOX

UNION COLLEGE

THE RONALD PRESS COMPANY • NEW YORK

Library of Congress Catalog Card Number: 63–10639

Preface

One of the problems presented to colleges by the changing pattern of science and technology is the place of numerical computation in the curriculum. The present book is written for a one-semester course to follow at least two years of calculus and differential equations. It concentrates special attention, in a single course, on the numerical aspects of problems of various types. Many problems encountered at this level present to the student for the first time the idea that a solution in closed form representing all points of interest may not follow from any of the carefully learned techniques of the calculus. He will find that techniques for solving systems of hundreds of equations are very different from the classical Cramer's rule. The fact that most applied problems, unlike the usual textbook problems, seem to fall in this "unsolvable" category is difficult to establish because of the student's lack of experience.

The increased complexity of applied mathematical problems, which are of direct interest to practicing scientists and engineers particularly, has been influenced to a great extent by the availability of automatic computers with high speed and large memory to carry out the routine phases of the solution once the form of the problems has been set up. Since almost all such computations are the result of point-by-point numerical analysis, considerable attention to these methods in the past decade has resulted in improvements on old techniques and in many new ones. Some important parts of these methods, such as error analysis and convergence criteria, may depend on mathematical levels well beyond the one for which this book is intended, and hence a restriction must be placed on the scope of the problems considered at this time. It is proper in a one-semester course, however, to consider topics of various degrees of difficulty on the basis of the better-known numerical methods, with appropriate references to journals describing recent significant developments. Some of the examples and exercises are related to theoretical studies of precision in the methods under consideration Others involve the use of these methods in the solution of applied problems from several different fields.

The material in this book has been classroom-tested by juniors and seniors at Union College. It is recommended that three weeks be devoted to each of the chapters on systems of linear algebraic equations, and ordinary and partial differential equations, and one week to each of the others. Adaptability to electronic computers is a foremost consideration in the selection of topics, although programing techniques are not specifically covered here. For the computation required in the problems, however, a desk calculator is always adequate.

AUGUSTUS H. FOX

Schenectady, N.Y.
January, 1963

Contents

FUNDAMENTALS OF
NUMERICAL ANALYSIS

1

Introduction

1-1. ROUNDOFF

Mathematics for most people starts with arithmetic, and operations more complicated than addition or multiplication are used relatively infrequently. In college courses in calculus and analytic geometry many students get the idea that the mathematics of the problem is independent of the arithmetic involved in the numerical result. It is a fact, however, that calculation of numerical results may involve very advanced mathematical techniques, and the development of these techniques is an important branch of mathematics. The representation of numbers in the decimal notation, for example, presents one opportunity for advanced analysis. Since finite numbers of decimal places must be used in representing irrational results, a rule must be used to determine the digit in the last place of the finite decimal. This roundoff rule usually involves using a smaller or a larger number, of the required number of digits, whichever is nearer the actual number in value. When the decimal representation of a number ends exactly in 5, but it is necessary to round off to one less decimal, another rule is involved. The choice to be made in treating a value halfway between two bounds is related to some idea of averaging the roundoff so that statistically half the time the upper bound is used and half the time the lower is used. Statistical estimation itself involves advanced mathematical techniques, but the rule resulting from such analysis involves some chance determination of the choice to be made. One such rule assumes that the probability of rounding to an even digit is equal to $\frac{1}{2}$, and hence half the time this will involve rounding upward, and half the time downward. The rule rounds every such number to an even last digit. Another statement of this rule involves the digit to the left of the 5; if this is odd, round upward; and if it is even, round downward. Studies of the operation of such rules have made no

3

"best" determination,[F2][H1]* so we will calculate answers in this book according to this rule. For example, 1.3675 is rounded to 1.368, while 1.3665 is rounded to 1.366.

1–2. ERRORS

The various techniques of numerical calculation were first aimed at assisting a person in carrying out intricate systems of addition and multiplication with a minimum of error in a reasonable time. These hand calculations are greatly modified by the use of the desk computer, which increases the number of significant figures that can be carried with ease, and cuts down the tedium of multiplications and divisions by automatic mechanical operations. In addition to the convenience of having more decimal places to work with, the reduction of time required for individual operations opens the way to solution of more extensive problems with the aid of a desk computer. Electronic computers increase the scope of these operations almost without limit.

Another aspect of computing techniques, however, involves the choice of a method appropriate to the problem, or the modification of the problem to make a well-known method applicable. Since the time involved in a complicated problem might involve several man-days, it becomes necessary to carry out an analysis of various methods both as to efficiency and as to relative accuracy of the result. If such an analysis can be made in less time than the computation, the over-all solution of the problem will be carried out as effectively as the ability of the computer permits. An important part of such an analysis involves the errors introduced, either of necessity by the details of the method or accidentally by the operator or the computer itself. These error analyses, depending on the number of operations involved, go well beyond the methods of checking used in previous pencil-and-paper calculations. A more complicated method with fewer steps may involve less opportunity for error than a simpler method that involves many more individual calculations. This leads to the use of more advanced mathematical tools, some of which have previously been applied to a method or to its analysis, but which are not in wide use. An example of this is the use of Gaussian techniques in quadrature problems in place of the more familiar trapezoidal or Simpson's rules.

The errors involved in many of the methods can be divided into two classes, *roundoff* errors and *truncation* errors. Individual multiplications or divisions of numbers whose last place is not known exactly may provide less precision in their outcomes. For example, the product of

* These superscript letters indicate items in the *References* at the end of the book.

.333 by .143 is .047619.   If these numbers are considered as the rounded values of the two factors, we know only that the correct product lies between .0473125 and .04785725.   Since this range determines precisely only the first significant figure in the product although we seemed to have three figures in each factor, we see that more places in the factors would be needed to arrive at three-place accuracy in the multiplication. The fact that the calculation gives five of the significant figures in the product of $\frac{1}{3}$ by $\frac{1}{7}$ is the type of accident that leads one to demand an analysis of roundoff errors.   When many such approximate multiplications and divisions are involved in the problem, it is certainly necessary to have some reason for assuming a particular level of precision for the answer.

The use of a digital computer may introduce another type of roundoff error due to the finite number of places that the machine can accommodate.   For example, in multiplying two 10-digit numbers, the product may contain 20 digits, but if the machine can accommodate only 10 digits, the product must be rounded off.   Another example comes in a computation of the sum or difference of two numbers each of which may involve ten significant digits individually.   When the decimal point is located differently in the two numbers, the smaller must be shifted in position and some of its digits lost.   For example, in the sum of 364875.2164 and 253.4687423, when the decimal points are lined up, the second number will automatically be rounded to 000253.4687.

A problem of machine calculation, called *overflow* on a fixed-point machine, is the result of the limited number of places to the left of the decimal point.   If a number greater than the capacity of the machine arises during a calculation, the extra digits are lost, and hence it is necessary to avoid this possibility.   Sometimes it is possible to scale all numbers by dividing by powers of 10 to avoid such overflow.   Since this is equivalent to shifting the number with respect to the decimal point, it involves the loss of digits at the right.   Scaling also implies the existence of a rough approximation of each step ahead of time in order to establish the minimum shift necessary.

Machines with floating-point operation write numbers in the scientific notation of the form $m \times 10^n$.   If a digit and a sign are used for indicating the characteristic n, and eight digits for the mantissa m, a number between 0 and 1, the system will accommodate all numbers between 10^{-10} and 10^9.   Another method, which substitutes $k = n + 5$ as the characteristic, will list all numbers between 10^{-5} and 10^4 with positive values of k, which eliminates the sign of the characteristic and adds one digit to the mantissa.   Floating-point operation will increase the scope of multiplications and divisions without overflow, but it is still necessary to add and subtract numbers with similar characteristics.   Many of the larger computer systems have built-in floating-point computation, and such special routines are available for floating point on others. This procedure increases the time of operation in built-in systems, and involves many extra orders in others, so that a compromise is involved in its use. For problems of known magnitudes, scaling with a fixed-point system is usually shorter, and easier to follow for finding possible mistakes.

1-3. CONDITION OF SYSTEMS

A similar loss of precision appears in the solution of some systems of linear equations. The need for careful study of techniques involving the solution of systems of equations arises from at least two sources. One is the effect of small errors in the coefficients on the value of the variable satisfying the system of equations. The other is the facility with which a method can be adapted to large numbers of variables and equations, since systems involving hundreds of simultaneous equations are common in some modern problems. In one system a small change in a coefficient makes only a slight change in the solution. Such systems are said to be *well conditioned*. In other cases, however, the relative change in the solution may be extremely large as a result of only a small relative change in the coefficients. Such systems are said to be *ill conditioned*. There obviously is no clearly marked line separating well- and ill-conditioned systems. This difficulty is combined with errors due to roundoffs appearing in the numerical calculations. The roundoff of a product involving a coefficient influences the solution just as a slight change in the value of the coefficient would.

Example 1-1. To illustrate conditioning, let us consider systems of two equations in two unknowns. For a well-conditioned example we take

$$300x + 400y = 700$$
$$100x + 100y = 200$$

for which the values $x = 1$ and $y = 1$ form the unique solution set.

If we change to the system

$$303x + 400y = 700$$
$$101x + 100y = 200$$

the solution changes to $x = 100/101 \cong .99$, $y = 1$. Thus a change of 1 per cent in coefficients produces a change of 1 per cent in the solution.

We now consider the ill-conditioned system,

$$300x + 400y = 700$$
$$100x + 133y = 233,$$

for which, also, the solution is $x = 1$, $y = 1$. Various small changes give the systems

$$\text{(a)} \quad 300x + 400y = 700$$
$$100x + 133y = 232,$$

and

$$\text{(b)} \quad 300x + 400y = 700$$
$$100x + 132y = 233,$$

and

$$\text{(c)} \quad 300x + 400y = 700$$
$$100x + 132y = 234.$$

The solutions for these systems, involving changes of a fraction of a per cent in the coefficients, are respectively

$$\text{(a)} \quad x = -3, y = 4,$$

and

$$\text{(b)} \quad x = 2, y = \frac{1}{4},$$

and

$$\text{(c)} \quad x = 3, y = -\frac{1}{2}.$$

Here the relative changes in the solutions are of the order of hundreds of per cent, and differ among themselves by an order of magnitude.

Example 1-2. To illustrate the effect of roundoff errors, consider the example

$$\frac{3}{4}x + \frac{1}{10}y = 1$$
$$\frac{9}{2}x + \frac{4}{7}y = 1.$$

If we use rational numbers, the solution is $x = -22; y = 175$. In the process of calculation, we may express each of the numbers involved except $\frac{4}{7}$ as a terminating decimal. If we carry only two places in the calculations, rounding off $\frac{4}{7}$ to .57 and $\frac{3}{7}$ to .43, we find the values $x = -23.5$, $y = 187.5$ as the result of the computation. If we carry three places of decimals, the result of the computation is $x = -21.4$, $y = 170$. These errors of several per cent of the true solution arise from individual roundoff errors of less than 1 per cent.

1-4. TRUNCATION ERROR

Truncation error results from the impossibility of calculating and combining an infinite set of terms in a series, or another extended set of operations, and sometimes even a large number of terms has to be reduced to a few for some practical reason. If such a reduced formula is repeated several times within a single calculation, it is sometimes found that the build-up of error resulting from truncation alone is intolerable even when each individual step is within a prescribed tolerance. For example, the substitution of small segments of tangent lines for the graph of a solution of a differential equation is a classical graphical method of representing a solution. The straight line pictures the truncation of the series expansion of the solution to two terms, and the error for a small step may be controlled by the size of the step.

Example 1–3. In the differential system $y' = -y$, $y(0) = 1$, first approximation would be $y_1 = 1 - x$ with a truncation error of less than $x^2/2$. If we take a step of $h = \frac{1}{10}$, the value of y_1 is .9000, with an error of less than .005. The next step involves

$$y_2 = .9 - (x - .1).9$$

and another step of $\frac{1}{10}$ gives $y_2 = .81$. Successive steps of this type give the approximate solution indicated in Table 1–1. The truncation error here is

TABLE 1–1

x	y_i	y	Error
0	1.0000		
.1	.9000		
.2	.8100		
.3	.7290		
.4	.6561		
.5	.5905	.6065	.0160
.6	.5315		
.7	.4783		
.8	.4305		
.9	.3875		
1.0	.3487	.3679	.0192

less than $h^2y/2$ at each step, and we see that the accumulated truncation error conforms to this limit.

Let us now use a formula derived from Simpson's quadrature rule, which is geometrically equivalent to substituting segments of parabolas in place of the line segments in the previous method. This formula will be developed in Chapter 5. Set

$$y_{n+1} = y_{n-1} + \frac{h}{3} (y'_{n+1} + 4y'_n + y'_{n-1})$$

with truncation error less than $h^5 y^v/90$.

Example 1–4. Using the differential system $y' = -y$, $y(0) = 1$, we have

$$y_{n+1} = y_{n-1} - \frac{h}{3}(y_{n+1} + 4y_n + y_{n-1})$$

$$\left(1 + \frac{h}{3}\right) y_{n+1} = \left(1 - \frac{h}{3}\right) y_{n-1} - \frac{4h}{3} y_n.$$

Solving for y_{n+1}, we get

$$y_{n+1} = \frac{3-h}{3+h} y_{n-1} - \frac{4h}{3+h} y_n.$$

Let us choose a large interval, $h = 1$, and start with the exact value $y_0 = 1$, $y_1 = .367879$. Our difference equation gives

$$y_{n+1} = \frac{y_{n-1}}{2} - y_n,$$

with a truncation error of less than $|y|/90$. The result appears in Table 1–2.

TABLE 1–2

		Error
$y_2 =$	.132121	.005214
$y_3 =$	.051819	$-.002032$
$y_4 =$	.014241	.004075
$y_5 =$	.011669	$-.004931$
$y_6 =$	$-.004549$	.007028

Beyond y_2 the error oscillates in sign and is larger than the accumulated truncation errors might indicate. Hence there is some other source of error build-up. This propagation of errors requires careful analysis, which will be given in Chapter 6.

EXERCISES

1–1. Investigate the effect on the solution of the following equations when the coefficient of y and the constant term in the second equation of each pair are increased by 1 to form three new systems:

a. $250x + 441y = 691$
   $123x + 217y = 340.$

b. $435x + 204y = 537$
   $221x + 104y = 294.$

c. $112x + 357y = 231$
   $209x + 666y = 431.$

1–2. Investigate the effect of roundoff error in approximating the rational coefficients of the following systems by one- or two-place decimals:

a. $\dfrac{2}{3}x + \dfrac{3}{5}y = 1$

$\dfrac{3}{2}x + \dfrac{6}{5}y = 1.$

b. $\dfrac{1}{2}x + \dfrac{1}{3}y = 3$

$\dfrac{3}{4}x + \dfrac{4}{7}y = 6.$

c. $\dfrac{7}{2}x + \dfrac{8}{5}y = 3$

$\dfrac{3}{2}x + \dfrac{2}{3}y = 1.$

1–3. Compare the results of applying the Simpson's rule method to the solution of the following equations with the exact solutions. Approximate the solutions to $x = 5$. Take $h = 1$.

a. $\dfrac{dy}{dx} = -\dfrac{1}{4}y,\ y(0) = 5,\ y(1) = 3.8940.$

b. $\dfrac{dy}{dx} = -\dfrac{xy}{5},\ y(0) = 1,\ y(1) = .9048.$

c. $\dfrac{dy}{dx} = -\dfrac{y}{x+1},\ y(0) = 2,\ y(1) = 1.$

2

Systems of Linear Algebraic Equations

2-1. TRIANGULAR FORM

A system of simultaneous linear algebraic equations has often been used as a model for some physical system in order to reduce a complex problem to a form whose solution is well known. Pencil-and-paper solutions of systems of a few equations have been taught in elementary algebra courses. More complicated solutions, often adapted to desk computer use, were developed as the number of equations increased.[T][H₁] The extension of these methods for digital computer solutions is not difficult, but in large systems decisions involving the rates of convergence and relative stability of different methods are introduced. Some of the algebraic analysis of these methods moves into fields of matrix theory beyond the scope of this book.[G][F₁] We shall also omit the interesting problems arising when the number of independent equations is different from the number of unknowns. The methods presented here are illustrated by systems of three or four equations, but they are readily extended to larger systems without serious change.

One basic form of solution, attributed to Gauss, involves the reduction of a system of n equations in n unknowns to an equivalent system (one with the same solution) in triangular form. This new set, in the general case, consists of one equation in one unknown, another equation involving this first unknown and a second, and so on until the last equation contains all the n unknowns, resulting in a triangular form on the left side of the system. The solution of this form of the system then is relatively simple. The equation in one unknown may be solved first; then by substitution in the next equation a solution for another unknown is determined; and so on, by solving for one unknown at a time. If we start with the system,

$$a_{11}x_1 + a_{12}x_2 + \cdots + a_{1n}x_n = h_1$$
$$a_{21}x_1 + a_{22}x_2 + \cdots + a_{2n}x_n = h_2$$
$$\cdot \qquad \cdot \qquad\qquad \cdot \qquad \cdot$$
$$\cdot \qquad \cdot \qquad\qquad \cdot \qquad \cdot$$
$$\cdot \qquad \cdot \qquad\qquad \cdot \qquad \cdot$$
$$a_{n1}x_1 + a_{n2}x_2 + \cdots + a_{nn}x_n = h_n,$$

we wish to reduce it to the form

$$b_{11}x_1 + b_{12}x_2 + \cdots + b_{1n}x_n = c_1$$
$$b_{22}x_2 + \cdots + b_{2n}x_n = c_2$$
$$\cdot \qquad \cdot$$
$$\cdot \qquad \cdot$$
$$\cdot \qquad \cdot$$
$$b_{nn}x_n = c_n.$$

The steps involved in changing a given system into triangular form proceed by eliminating one variable at a time. Let us indicate the different sets of coefficients by superscripts:

$$b_{1k}^{(1)} = a_{1k} \ (k = 1, \ \ldots, n), c_1^{(1)} = h_1.$$

Then in order to get $b_{i1}^{(1)} = 0$ $(i = 2, \ldots, n)$, we must multiply the first equation by the factor $-a_{i1}/a_{11}$ and add to the ith equation. This determines all the other constants in the form

$$b_{ik}^{(1)} = a_{ik} - \frac{a_{i1}}{a_{11}} a_{1k} \ (i, k = 2, \ldots, n)$$
$$c_i^{(1)} = h_i - \frac{a_{i1}h_1}{a_{11}}.$$

Now we omit the first equation and treat the remaining equations in the same manner to get the set $b_{ik}^{(2)}$:

$$b_{2k}^{(2)} = b_{2k}^{(1)} \ (k = 2, \ \ldots, n), c_2^{(2)} = c_2^{(1)}$$
$$b_{i2}^{(2)} = 0 \ (i = 3, \ \ldots, n)$$
$$b_{ik}^{(2)} = b_{ik}^{(1)} - \frac{b_{i2}^{(1)}}{b_{22}^{(1)}} b_{2k}^{(2)}, c_i^{(2)} = c_i^{(1)} - \frac{b_{i2}^{(1)}}{b_{22}^{(1)}} c_2^{(1)}.$$

In this way we may proceed in $n - 1$ steps to determine the triangular form for any set of equations, provided none of the diagonal terms $b_{kk}^{(k-1)}$ is zero. We write the final set of constants and coefficients without superscripts, as in the triangular form shown above.

The solution of the equations in triangular form then proceeds from the last to the first:

$$x_n = \frac{c_n}{b_{nn}},$$

$$x_{n-1} = \frac{c_{n-1} - b_{n-1\,n}x_n}{b_{n-1\,n-1}},$$

$$x_k = \frac{c_k - x_n b_{kn} - x_{n-1}b_{k\,n-1} - \cdots - x_{k+1}b_{k\,k+1}}{b_{kk}} \quad (k = 1, \ldots, n-2).$$

Example 2–1. Let us consider the equations,

$$\begin{aligned}
x_1 + 3x_2 + 4x_3 + x_4 &= 7 \\
2x_1 + 5x_2 + 3x_3 - 2x_4 &= 10 \\
x_1 + 4x_2 + 6x_3 - x_4 &= 8 \\
2x_1 + 2x_2 - x_3 + 2x_4 &= 3.
\end{aligned}$$

Here the elimination of the x_1 variable results in the first set $b_{ik}^{(1)}$:

$$\begin{aligned}
x_1 + 3x_2 + 4x_3 + x_4 &= 7 \\
- x_2 - 5x_3 - 4x_4 &= -4 \\
x_2 + 2x_3 - 2x_4 &= 1 \\
- 4x_2 - 9x_3 \phantom{{}- 2x_4} &= -11.
\end{aligned}$$

The second set $b_{ik}^{(2)}$ then is determined in the last three equations:

$$\begin{aligned}
x_1 + 3x_2 + 4x_3 + x_4 &= 7 \\
- x_2 - 5x_3 - 4x_4 &= -4 \\
- 3x_3 - 6x_4 &= -3 \\
11x_3 + 16x_4 &= 5.
\end{aligned}$$

The final set and the triangular form is

$$\begin{aligned}
x_1 + 3x_2 + 4x_3 + x_4 &= 7 \\
- x_2 - 5x_3 - 4x_4 &= -4 \\
- 3x_3 - 6x_4 &= -3 \\
- 6x_4 &= -6.
\end{aligned}$$

Then back-substitution determines the solution,

$$x_4 = 1, \; x_3 = -1, \; x_2 = 5, \; x_1 = -5.$$

In the process of changing a system to triangular form, division by the diagonal coefficients $b_{kk}^{(k-1)}$ is an essential part of the method. Hence none of these coefficients may vanish, and errors in the solution are magnified by very small values of the b_{kk}. The necessary and sufficient condition for the existence of the solution of the system is the non-vanishing of the determinant of the coefficients of the variables. When this condition theorem is applied to the triangular form of the system, it is found that the determinant is merely the product of the diagonal terms $b_{11}b_{22} \cdots b_{nn}$. The determinant is changed by a constant factor in the steps involved in the reduction to triangular form, so that the non-vanishing of the b_{kk} also governs the existence of a solution for the original system.[G]

Whenever the b_{kk} are small compared with the expressions into which they are divided, errors of computation may be increased. This is mainly due to the fact that differences are involved between the numbers thus generated and other constants in the system, and frequently the number of significant figures retained may be decreased in such calculations. In many systems it is possible to reorganize the set of equations, or the labeling of the unknowns, so as to avoid small values of b_{kk} early in the calculations. One way of achieving this result is to find the term with the largest coefficient among the equations remaining to be changed in the kth step, and to shift this term to the $b_{kk}^{(k-1)}$ position by interchanging equations and unknowns. This process of chosing the *pivotal* coefficient is easy to accomplish in hand computations, but is difficult to program for a computer, principally in identifying the ultimate variables with those in the original equations.[O] One technique for handling ill-conditioned systems involves the arbitrary introduction of increments to the diagonal terms a_{kk} to avoid zero values of the corresponding b_{kk}. Then an analysis of the system with these increased diagonal coefficients makes possible more accurate solutions of the ill-conditioned system.[C]

2–2. MATRIX FACTORIZATION

The type of numerical operations involved in the reduction to triangular form may be organized in a different way by the use of matrices. We assume a knowledge of the process of matrix multiplication. The system of equations

$$\sum_{k=1}^{n} a_{ik}x_k = h_i \ (i = 1, \ldots, n)$$

may be written in matrix notation

$$AX = H$$

with $A = (a_{ik})$, the $n \times n$ matrix of coefficients, and X and H n-rowed column vectors. We intend to modify this equation by factoring the matrix A into factors, one a matrix with all elements above the diagonal zero, and the other with all elements below the diagonal zero. The possibility of doing this is suggested, but not proved, by the following discussion. The factors have $2n^2$ elements which must satisfy only n^2 conditions involved in making the product identical with the original matrix A. Since there are only $n^2 - n$ zeroes involved in the two triangular matrices, a further set of n choices may be applied. We will use these choices to make the diagonal elements in one of the factors all 1's. Thus we have the problem of determining n^2 elements in the two factors from the n^2 equations, each obtained from the product of the elements of a row of the first factor and a column of the second factor. The advantage of the triangular form is that the elements in these factors may be determined sequentially one at a time for the corresponding equations. We proceed as follows:

$$LU = A$$

$$\begin{pmatrix} L_{11} & 0 & 0 \\ L_{21} & L_{22} & 0 \\ L_{31} & L_{32} & L_{33} \end{pmatrix} \begin{pmatrix} 1 & U_{12} & U_{13} \\ 0 & 1 & U_{23} \\ 0 & 0 & 1 \end{pmatrix} = \begin{pmatrix} a_{11} & a_{12} & a_{13} \\ a_{21} & a_{22} & a_{23} \\ a_{31} & a_{32} & a_{33} \end{pmatrix}.$$

If we use the rows of the first factor and the first column of the second, we find

$$L_{11} = a_{11}, \ L_{21} = a_{21}, \ L_{31} = a_{31}.$$

The first column of the L matrix is identical with the first column of A. Then the first row and the other columns of the second factor give

$$L_{11}U_{12} = a_{12}, \ L_{11}U_{13} = a_{13}.$$

Hence

$$U_{12} = \frac{a_{12}}{a_{11}}, \ U_{13} = \frac{a_{13}}{a_{11}}.$$

The first row of the U matrix involves the elements of the first row of A divided by a_{11}. Now we use the other rows of the first factor and the second column to get

$$L_{21}U_{12} + L_{22} = a_{22}, \ L_{22} = a_{22} - \frac{a_{21}a_{12}}{a_{11}},$$

$$L_{31}U_{12} + L_{32} = a_{32}, \ L_{32} = a_{32} - \frac{a_{31}a_{12}}{a_{11}}.$$

The remaining elements then are given by the equations

$$L_{21}U_{13} + L_{22}U_{23} = a_{23}, \ U_{23} = \frac{a_{23} - L_{21}U_{13}}{L_{22}},$$

$$L_{31}U_{13} + L_{32}U_{23} + L_{33} = a_{33}, \ L_{33} = a_{33} - L_{32}U_{23} - L_{31}U_{13}.$$

Although this formal factorization procedure does not entirely establish the conditions, it may be carried out whenever the determinant of the matrix is not zero.[G]   Such matrices are called *non-singular* matrices.

Example 2-2.   For example we factor the matrix of the system

$$x_1 + 3x_2 + 4x_3 = 6$$
$$2x_1 + 5x_2 + 3x_3 = 12$$
$$x_1 + 4x_2 + 6x_3 = 9.$$

Here,

$$A = \begin{pmatrix} 1 & 3 & 4 \\ 2 & 5 & 3 \\ 1 & 4 & 6 \end{pmatrix},$$

and we can write immediately

$$L = \begin{pmatrix} 1 & 0 & 0 \\ 2 & L_{22} & 0 \\ 1 & L_{32} & L_{33} \end{pmatrix}, \quad U = \begin{pmatrix} 1 & 3 & 4 \\ 0 & 1 & U_{23} \\ 0 & 0 & 1 \end{pmatrix}.$$

We first get the equations

$$6 + L_{22} = 5,\ L_{22} = -1,$$

and

$$3 + L_{32} = 4,\ L_{32} = 1.$$

Then

$$8 - U_{23} = 3,\ U_{23} = 5,$$

and

$$4 + 5 + L_{33} = 6,\ L_{33} = -3.$$

Hence

$$\begin{pmatrix} 1 & 3 & 4 \\ 2 & 5 & 3 \\ 1 & 4 & 6 \end{pmatrix} = \begin{pmatrix} 1 & 0 & 0 \\ 2 & -1 & 0 \\ 1 & 1 & -3 \end{pmatrix} \begin{pmatrix} 1 & 3 & 4 \\ 0 & 1 & 5 \\ 0 & 0 & 1 \end{pmatrix}.$$

The factor matrices are then used separately in determining the solution of the equations.   The two matrix equations, $LY = H$, $UX = Y$, are equivalent to the original equation $AX = L(UX) = H$.   We solve for Y in the first of these, one variable at a time, in the form

$$\begin{pmatrix} L_{11} & 0 & 0 \\ L_{21} & L_{22} & 0 \\ L_{31} & L_{32} & L_{33} \end{pmatrix} \begin{pmatrix} Y_1 \\ Y_2 \\ Y_3 \end{pmatrix} = \begin{pmatrix} H_1 \\ H_2 \\ H_3 \end{pmatrix},$$

$$L_{11}Y_1 = H_1,\ Y_1 = \frac{H_1}{L_{11}},$$

$$L_{21}Y_1 + L_{22}Y_2 = H_2,\ Y_2 = \frac{H_2 - L_{21}H_1/L_{11}}{L_{22}},$$

$$L_{31}Y_1 + L_{32}Y_2 + L_{33}Y_3 = H_3,\ Y_3 = \frac{H_3 - L_{32}Y_2 - L_{31}Y_1}{L_{33}}.$$

Then we repeat this process in the second set, starting with the last equation:

$$\begin{pmatrix} 1 & U_{12} & U_{13} \\ 0 & 1 & U_{23} \\ 0 & 0 & 1 \end{pmatrix} \begin{pmatrix} X_1 \\ X_2 \\ X_3 \end{pmatrix} = \begin{pmatrix} Y_1 \\ Y_2 \\ Y_3 \end{pmatrix},$$

$$X_3 = Y_3,$$
$$X_2 + U_{23}X_3 = Y_2, \; X_2 = Y_2 - U_{23}Y_3,$$
$$X_1 + U_{12}X_2 + U_{13}X_3 = Y_1, \; X_1 = Y_1 - U_{12}X_2 - U_{13}X_3.$$

This method of solution involves a number of steps, all sequential, in which one unknown at a time is determined. None of the steps depends in an essential way on the number of equations in the system. The only effect of larger systems is to make more numerous the same kind of operations in some of the steps. With a computer or a desk calculator, this process may be carried out for large systems of equations.

Example 2–3. We apply this method to the set of equations whose matrix we factored:

$$\begin{pmatrix} 1 & 0 & 0 \\ 2 & -1 & 0 \\ 1 & 1 & -3 \end{pmatrix} \begin{pmatrix} y_1 \\ y_2 \\ y_3 \end{pmatrix} = \begin{pmatrix} 6 \\ 12 \\ 9 \end{pmatrix},$$

$$y_1 = 6,$$
$$12 - y_2 = 12, \; y_2 = 0,$$
$$6 + 0 - 3y_3 = 9, \; y_3 = -1.$$

Then

$$\begin{pmatrix} 1 & 3 & 4 \\ 0 & 1 & 5 \\ 0 & 0 & 1 \end{pmatrix} \begin{pmatrix} x_1 \\ x_2 \\ x_3 \end{pmatrix} = \begin{pmatrix} 6 \\ 0 \\ -1 \end{pmatrix}$$

$$x_3 = -1$$
$$x_2 - 5 = 0, \; x_2 = 5,$$
$$x_1 + 3(5) - 4 = 6, \; x_1 = -5.$$

2–3. MATRIX INVERSION

When the same matrix of coefficients is to be used with a number of different sets of constants H, the solution may be speeded up by solving for the inverse of the matrix A. The equation

$$AX = H$$

is solved in the form

$$X = A^{-1}H.$$

The inverse of the matrix A, is a matrix A^{-1} such that $A^{-1}A = I$, where I is the unit matrix of order n, with the diagonal elements all 1's and all other elements zeroes. Its determination is equivalent to solving the n^2 equations involved in the product $A^{-1}A$ for the n^2 elements in the inverse matrix. Here again, the necessary condition for such a solution is the non-vanishing of the determinant of the matrix. Hence the inverse exists only for a non-singular matrix. In order to make this solution sequential, we use the triangular factors of the matrix. The inverse of the product LU is the product of the inverses in the reverse order $U^{-1}L^{-1}$, since

$$U^{-1}L^{-1}LU = U^{-1}IU = U^{-1}U = I.$$

The inverse of L involves the matrix equation

$$\begin{pmatrix} \Gamma_{11} & \Gamma_{12} & \Gamma_{13} \\ \Gamma_{21} & \Gamma_{22} & \Gamma_{23} \\ \Gamma_{31} & \Gamma_{32} & \Gamma_{33} \end{pmatrix} \begin{pmatrix} L_{11} & 0 & 0 \\ L_{21} & L_{22} & 0 \\ L_{31} & L_{32} & L_{32} \end{pmatrix} = \begin{pmatrix} 1 & 0 & 0 \\ 0 & 1 & 0 \\ 0 & 0 & 1 \end{pmatrix}.$$

If we consider the product of the first row and the last column we have $\Gamma_{13}L_{33} = 0$ and $\Gamma_{13} = 0$. Then the product of the second row and the last column gives $\Gamma_{23}L_{33} = 0$ and $\Gamma_{23} = 0$. The product of the first row and the next to the last column gives $\Gamma_{12}L_{22} + \Gamma_{13}L_{33} = 0$ and $\Gamma_{12} = 0$. In general, it can be shown that the inverse of any triangular matrix is a triangular matrix of the same form.

Next we consider the diagonal elements involved in products of similar rows and columns:

$$\Gamma_{11}L_{11} + \Gamma_{12}L_{21} + \Gamma_{13}L_{31} = 1 \text{ and } \Gamma_{11} = \frac{1}{L_{11}},$$

$$\Gamma_{22}L_{22} + \Gamma_{23}L_{32} = 1 \text{ and } \Gamma_{22} = \frac{1}{L_{22}},$$

$$\Gamma_{33}L_{33} = 1 \text{ and } \Gamma_{33} = \frac{1}{L_{33}}.$$

Thus the diagonal elements of the inverse of a triangular matrix are the reciprocals of the corresponding diagonal elements of the matrix. We then need to solve only enough equations to determine the non-zero off-diagonal elements in the inverse. The last row and the next-to-last column give

$$\Gamma_{32}L_{22} + \Gamma_{33}L_{32} = 0, \ \Gamma_{32} = -\frac{L_{32}}{L_{33}L_{22}}.$$

Then the last row and the first column give

$$\Gamma_{31}L_{11} + \Gamma_{32}L_{21} + \Gamma_{33}L_{31} = 0,$$
$$\Gamma_{31} = \frac{-L_{31}/L_{33} + L_{21}L_{32}/L_{33}L_{22}}{L_{11}}.$$

Finally the second row and the first column determine Γ_{21} in a similar form. Again this sequential procedure is independent of the order of the matrix.   A corresponding procedure applies to the inversion of the upper triangular matrix U.   Then the product of U^{-1} and Γ involves n^2 steps to determine the elements in the matrix A^{-1}.   In terms of this matrix, then, the solution for the variables involves the n steps in multiplying A^{-1} into the column vector H.

Example 2-4.   To invert L in the example in Art. 2-2, we can write

$$\begin{pmatrix} 1 & 0 & 0 \\ \Gamma_{21} & -1 & 0 \\ \Gamma_{31} & \Gamma_{32} & -\dfrac{1}{3} \end{pmatrix} \begin{pmatrix} 1 & 0 & 0 \\ 2 & -1 & 0 \\ 1 & 1 & -3 \end{pmatrix} = \begin{pmatrix} 1 & 0 & 0 \\ 0 & 1 & 0 \\ 0 & 0 & 1 \end{pmatrix}.$$

From row 2,

$$\Gamma_{21} - 2 = 0, \Gamma_{21} = 2.$$

From row 3,

$$-\Gamma_{32} - \frac{1}{3} = 0, \Gamma_{32} = -\frac{1}{3}$$

$$\Gamma_{31} + 2\Gamma_{32} - \frac{1}{3} = 0, \Gamma_{31} = 1$$

$$\Gamma = \begin{pmatrix} 1 & 0 & 0 \\ 2 & -1 & 0 \\ 1 & -\dfrac{1}{3} & -\dfrac{1}{3} \end{pmatrix}.$$

Similarly

$$U^{-1} = \begin{pmatrix} 1 & -3 & 11 \\ 0 & 1 & -5 \\ 0 & 0 & 1 \end{pmatrix}$$

then

$$A^{-1} = U^{-1}\Gamma$$

$$= \begin{pmatrix} 1 & -3 & 11 \\ 0 & 1 & -5 \\ 0 & 0 & 1 \end{pmatrix} \begin{pmatrix} 1 & 0 & 0 \\ 2 & -1 & 0 \\ 1 & -\dfrac{1}{3} & -\dfrac{1}{3} \end{pmatrix}$$

$$= \begin{pmatrix} 6 & -\dfrac{2}{3} & -\dfrac{11}{3} \\ -3 & \dfrac{2}{3} & \dfrac{5}{3} \\ 1 & -\dfrac{1}{3} & -\dfrac{1}{3} \end{pmatrix},$$

and

$$\begin{pmatrix} 6 & -\dfrac{2}{3} & -\dfrac{11}{3} \\ -3 & \dfrac{2}{3} & \dfrac{5}{3} \\ 1 & -\dfrac{1}{3} & -\dfrac{1}{3} \end{pmatrix} \begin{pmatrix} 6 \\ 12 \\ 9 \end{pmatrix} = \begin{pmatrix} -5 \\ 5 \\ -1 \end{pmatrix}.$$

The solution is $x_1 = -5$, $x_2 = 5$, $x_3 = -1$.

The method of inversion can be employed effectively if many sets of constants H are to be used. In addition, this method of determining the inverse of a matrix A may be used even when no equations are involved since the inverse of a matrix is used in other matrix operations.[G]

2-4. EFFECT OF ERRORS

In order to illustrate the effect of errors in the constants, let us consider the error produced in the solution by an uncertainty in the constants H_i of unknown sign, and of magnitude e_i. We assume no errors in the coefficients, and no roundoff errors in the inversion process. Hence we may write

$$A(X + \Delta X) = H + E$$
$$X + \Delta X = A^{-1}(H + E).$$

Since $X = A^{-1}H$, we have $\Delta X = A^{-1}E$. These equations are ambiguous since the column vector E contains unknown signs. We can merely determine the maximum errors possible by the most unfavorable choice of signs.

Example 2-5. In the system treated in the example in Art. 2-2, suppose that the constant terms are uncertain to $\pm.05$.

Then the corresponding errors in the variables are given by

$$\begin{pmatrix} \Delta x \\ \Delta y \\ \Delta z \end{pmatrix} = \begin{pmatrix} 6 & -\dfrac{2}{3} & -\dfrac{11}{3} \\ -3 & \dfrac{2}{3} & \dfrac{5}{3} \\ 1 & -\dfrac{1}{3} & -\dfrac{1}{3} \end{pmatrix} \begin{pmatrix} \pm.05 \\ \pm.05 \\ \pm.05 \end{pmatrix},$$

$$|\Delta x| \le \left(6 + \dfrac{2}{3} + \dfrac{11}{3}\right).05 = \dfrac{31}{60} \cong .5,$$

$$|\Delta y| \le \left(3 + \dfrac{2}{3} + \dfrac{5}{3}\right).05 = \dfrac{4}{15} \cong .27,$$

$$|\Delta z| \le \left(1 + \dfrac{1}{3} + \dfrac{1}{3}\right).05 = \dfrac{1}{12} \cong .08.$$

Then the best we can say for the solution of this system is roughly

$$-5.5 \le x \le -4.5,$$
$$4.73 \le y \le 5.27,$$
$$-1.08 \le z \le -0.92.$$

The errors in the constants are relatively small, less than 1 per cent in each case. The uncertainties in the solution in this example are much greater, and amount to as much as 10 per cent of the computed values. Since the error .05

represents the maximum roundoff error in determining the first decimal, we might increase the precision of the constants to the second place. The corresponding uncertain solution then would be good to the first decimal place:

$$-5.06 < x < -4.94,$$
$$4.97 < y < 5.03,$$
$$-1.01 < z < -0.99.$$

Corresponding discussions of the uncertainties introduced by errors in the coefficient matrix are much more complicated.[H₂]   The additional problem of the effect of roundoff errors on the inversion process is also beyond the scope of the present volume.   In fact the general discussion of these errors is one of the most active fields in this branch of mathematics.   Recent studies are covered in the references.[F₁][H₁]

2–5. GAUSS-SEIDEL ITERATION METHODS

Some systems of equations are easier to solve by successive approximations based on an original trial solution than by manipulating the many constants in their matrices.   This is especially true when the variables can be labeled in such a way that the constants in the diagonal terms are larger than any others in the matrix.   This method, also due to Gauss, involves each unknown in an equation of the form,

$$x_1 = \frac{h_1 - a_{12}x_2 - a_{13}x_3 - \cdots - a_{1n}x_n}{a_{11}}$$

$$x_2 = \frac{h_2 - a_{21}x_1 - a_{23}x_3 - \cdots - a_{2n}x_n}{a_{22}}$$

$$\vdots$$

$$x_n = \frac{h_n - a_{n1}x_1 - a_{n2}x_2 - \cdots - a_{n\,n-1}x_{n-1}}{a_{nn}}.$$

An assumed set of initial values of x's,

$$(x_1^{(0)}, x_2^{(0)}, \ldots, x_n^{(0)}),$$

is used on the right side to determine a second set of values,

$$(x_1^{(1)}, x_2^{(1)}, \ldots, x_n^{(1)}).$$

This operation is repeated until no further improvement is possible. The important question here is the convergence of the sets of approximations to the solution.

Example 2–6. As an example of this method, take the system

$$10x_1 + 2x_2 + 3x_3 - x_4 = 40$$
$$x_1 - 20x_2 - x_3 + 3x_4 = 20$$
$$x_1 + x_2 - 10x_3 + 2x_4 = 20$$
$$2x_1 - x_2 - x_3 + 30x_4 = 60.$$

Converting this to the iteration form, we have

$$x_1 = \frac{40 - 2x_2 - 3x_3 + x_4}{10}$$

$$x_2 = \frac{20 - x_1 + x_3 - 3x_4}{-20}$$

$$x_3 = \frac{20 - x_1 - x_2 - 2x_4}{-10}$$

$$x_4 = \frac{60 - 2x_1 + x_2 + x_3}{30}$$

Let us start with an initial set

$$x_1^{(0)} = x_2^{(0)} = x_3^{(0)} = x_4^{(0)} = 0.$$

Then

$$x_1^{(1)} = 4, \ x_2^{(1)} = -1, \ x_3^{(1)} = -2, \ x_4^{(1)} = 2.$$

The second approximation becomes

$$x_1^{(2)} = 5, \quad x_2^{(2)} = -.4, \quad x_3^{(2)} = -1.3, \ x_4^{(2)} = 1.6;$$

and the third

$$x_1^{(3)} = 4.6, \ x_2^{(3)} = -.44, \ x_3^{(3)} = -1.2, \ x_4^{(3)} = 1.6;$$

and the fourth

$$x_1^{(4)} = 4.6, \ x_2^{(4)} = -.47, \ x_3^{(4)} = -1.3, \ x_4^{(4)} = 1.6.$$

This solution seems to be correct to two significant figures. An improvement in the Gauss iteration method, due to Seidel, involves the use, at each step, of the latest computed value for the substituted variables, thus making use of more accurate values as they are calculated.

This improves the rate of convergence of the example, as follows, starting at the same null solution:

$$x_1^{(0)} = \quad x_2^{(0)} = \quad x_3^{(0)} = \quad x_4^{(0)} = 0;$$
$$x_1^{(1)} = 4, \ x_2^{(1)} = -.8, \ x_3^{(1)} = -1.7, \ x_4^{(1)} = 1.6;$$

then

$$x_1^{(2)} = 4.8, \ x_2^{(2)} = -.44, \ x_3^{(2)} = -1.24, \ x_4^{(2)} = 1.62;$$
$$x_1^{(3)} = 4.62, \ x_2^{(3)} = -.464, \ x_3^{(3)} = -1.26, \ x_4^{(3)} = 1.64;$$
$$x_1^{(4)} = 4.63, \ x_2^{(4)} = -.461, \ x_3^{(4)} = -1.26, \ x_4^{(4)} = 1.63.$$

Here, in four iterations we have a solution converging to three significant figures.

A method of improving the solution of a system such as that of Example 2–6 involves the use of a new set of constants obtained by changing the variables by subtracting the result of a previous approximation. If we set

$$y_1 = x_1 - x_1^{(k)}, \quad y_2 = x_2 - x_2^{(k)}, \quad \ldots, \quad y_n = x_n - x_n^{(k)},$$

and substitute in the system of equations, the new set of equations in the y's will involve the same coefficient matrix but a new, and smaller, set of constants.

Example 2–7. In the example, let us use the two-significant-figure result as our reference set. Then the new variables become:

$$y_1 = x_1 - 4.6,$$
$$y_2 = x_2 + .47,$$
$$y_3 = x_3 + 1.3,$$
$$y_4 = x_4 - 1.6.$$

The system of equations for y is

$$10y_1 + 2y_2 + 3y_3 - y_4 = .44$$
$$y_1 - 20y_2 - y_3 + 3y_4 = -.10$$
$$y_1 + y_2 - 10y_3 + 2y_4 = -.33$$
$$2y_1 - y_2 - y_3 + 30y_4 = 1.03.$$

The iteration form becomes

$$y_1 = \frac{.44 - 2y_2 - 2y_3 + y_4}{10}$$

$$y_2 = \frac{-.10 - y_1 + y_3 - 3y_4}{-20}$$

$$y_3 = \frac{-.33 - y_1 - y_2 - 2y_4}{-10}$$

$$y_4 = \frac{1.03 - 2y_1 + y_2 + y_3}{30}.$$

Starting with $y_k^{(0)}$ all 0, using the Seidel method, we get

$$y_1^{(1)} = .044, \quad y_2^{(1)} = .0072, \quad y_3^{(1)} = .038, \quad y_4^{(1)} = .033$$
$$y_1^{(2)} = .034, \quad y_2^{(2)} = .0098, \quad y_3^{(2)} = .044, \quad y_4^{(2)} = .037$$
$$y_1^{(3)} = .0325, \quad y_2^{(3)} = .0100, \quad y_3^{(3)} = .0446, \quad y_4^{(3)} = .0347$$
$$y_1^{(4)} = .0321, \quad y_2^{(4)} = .00958, \quad y_3^{(4)} = .0441, \quad y_4^{(4)} = .0340$$
$$y_1^{(5)} = .0322, \quad y_2^{(5)} = .00951, \quad y_3^{(5)} = .0440, \quad y_4^{(5)} = .0340.$$

Hence the solution of the original system is, to this order of approximation,

$$x_1 = 4.6322, \quad x_2 = -.46051, \quad x_3 = -1.2560, \quad x_4 = 1.6340.$$

2–6. ITERATION CONVERGENCE

In order to establish sufficient conditions under which these iteration methods converge, let us identify the solution of a system of the form of Art. 2–5 as $(\alpha_1, \alpha_2, \ldots, \alpha_n)$. Thus we can write the errors in any one iteration by $w_k = \alpha_k - x_k$. The system of equations for these errors is

$$-w_1 = \frac{a_{12}w_2 + a_{13}w_3 + \cdots + a_{1n}w_n}{a_{11}}$$

$$\vdots$$

$$-w_n = \frac{a_{n1}w_1 + a_{n2}w_2 + \cdots + a_{n\,n-1}w_{n-1}}{a_{nn}}.$$

When these are treated as iteration equations we designate the new values on the left side by w_k^*, and upon taking absolute values we have the inequalities,

$$|w_1^*| \leq \frac{|a_{12}|\,|w_2| + \cdots + |a_{1n}|\,|w_n|}{|a_{11}|}$$

$$\vdots$$

$$|w_n^*| \leq \frac{|a_{n1}|\,|w_1| + \cdots + |a_{n\,n-1}|\,|w_{n-1}|}{|a_{nn}|}.$$

By adding these, we obtain an inequality for the sum of the absolute errors in the new values in terms of the absolute errors in the old values, and a sufficient condition for convergence involves a definite decrease in this sum of absolute errors. Let us identify the sum of the absolute coefficients on the right side of each of these equations by a single symbol:

$$A_k = \frac{|a_{1k}| + |a_{2k}| + \cdots + |a_{nk}|}{|a_{kk}|},$$

where the coefficient $|a_{kk}|$ does not appear in the numerator term on the right. Then we write new inequalities,

$$|w_1^*| + |w_2^*| + \cdots + |w_n^*| \leq A_k(|w_1| + |w_2| + \cdots + |w_n|),$$

since for each k we have added to the right side new terms which are all non-negative. The condition for convergence is then that the A_k be bounded away from unity from below, $A_k \leq p < 1$. These conditions then may be written

$$|a_{k1}| + |a_{k2}| + \cdots + |a_{kn}| \leq p|a_{kk}|$$

where p is less than 1. This means that the diagonal terms dominate the absolute sum of the other elements in the corresponding columns. By rearrangement of terms, corresponding conditions applied to the elements of a row can also be shown to be sufficient for convergence of the Gauss and Gauss-Seidel iteration methods. Since these are not necessary conditions, border-line cases that fail in some respect to satisfy these conditions will still converge, and hence the method may be tried more widely than merely in systems with dominant diagonal terms. Another suggestion from these conditions is the ordering of the equations and the variables so that the diagonal coefficients are the largest in absolute values.

EXERCISES

Solve the following systems:

2-1. a. $x + 3y - 2z = 4$
$2x + 8y - 5z = 15$
$3x + y + 2z = 4.$

b. $x + 2y - z = 6$
$4x - 3y + z = 7$
$3x + y - 5z = 6.$

c. $6x - 5y + 9z = 10$
$5x + 4y - 3z = -15$
$8x - 2y + 7z = 3.$

2-2. a. $3.1x - 2.5y - 1.3z = 1.20$
$2.3x + 4.1y + 2.2z = 4.29$
$1.7x - 6.3y - 3.2z = 5.17.$

b. $2.6x - 3.1y + 4.3z = .41$
$5.4x + 2.7y - 7.3z = 47.30$
$4.3x - 6.2y + 1.5z = 10.96.$

c. $1.4x + 1.5y - 1.6z = 0.00$
$2.3x + 2.4y - 2.5z = 0.25$
$3.2x - 4.3y + 5.4z = 19.60.$

2-3. a. $x_1 + x_2 = 0.9$
$x_1 + 4x_2 + x_3 = 10.7$
$x_2 + 4x_3 + x_4 = 14.4$
$x_3 + x_4 = 1.8.$

b. $x_1 + x_2 = -1$
$x_1 + 4x_2 + 2x_3 = -1$
$2x_2 + 4x_3 + x_4 = 3$
$2x_3 + x_4 = 1.$

c. $x_1 + 2x_2 + 3x_3 + 4x_4 = 14.88$
$2x_1 + 3x_2 + 4x_3 + 5x_4 = 19.05$
$3x_1 + 2x_2 + x_3 - x_4 = 8.95$
$4x_1 - 3x_2 + 2x_3 + x_4 = -14.61.$

2-4. a. $62x_1 + 12x_2 + 9x_3 = 15$
$21x_1 + 74x_2 - 13x_3 = 25$
$19x_1 - 23x_2 + 86x_3 = 41.$

b. $125x_1 + 15x_2 + 8x_3 = 19$
$12x_1 + 165x_2 + 15x_3 = 24$
$22x_1 + 35x_2 - 135x_3 = 17.$

c. $32x_1 + 175x_2 - 12x_3 = 18$
$180x_1 + 11x_2 + 15x_3 = 25$
$31x_1 - 15x_2 + 220x_3 = 7.$

2-5. a. $1.7x + 3.1y - 2.5z = 4.5$
$2.1x - 7.5y + 5.3z = 6.2$
$3.7x - 4.3y - 8.1z = 2.7.$

b. $1.3x_1 + 2.4x_2 = 5.7$
$2.1x_1 + 3.2x_2 + 1.5x_3 = 8.5$
$1.1x_2 + 4.8x_3 + 1.2x_4 = 7.8$
$6.1x_3 + 3.2x_4 = 4.7.$

c. $165x_1 + 373x_2 = 680$
$215x_1 + 325x_2 + 149x_3 = 875$
$163x_2 + 643x_3 + 287x_4 = 968$
$401x_3 + 216x_4 = 587.$

2-6. a. $x_1 + x_2 = 5$
$x_1 + 4x_2 + x_3 = 7$
$x_2 + 4x_3 + x_4 = 9$
$x_3 + 4x_4 + x_5 = 11$
$x_4 + x_5 = 13.$

b. $x_1 + x_2 + x_3 = 5$
$2x_2 + 3x_3 - x_4 = -8$
$x_3 - 2x_4 + 3x_5 = 6$
$x_1 + 2x_3 + 3x_5 = 4$
$2x_2 + 4x_4 + x_5 = 7.$

c. $2x_1 + x_2 = 10$
$x_1 + 2x_2 + x_3 = 15$
$x_2 + 2x_3 + x_4 = 20$
$x_3 + 2x_4 + x_5 = 20$
$x_4 + 2x_5 + x_6 = 15$
$x_5 + 2x_6 = 10.$

2-7. When all the constants on the right side of a system of linear equations are zero, an obvious solution consists of zero values for each of the unknowns. The possibility of non-zero solutions arises when the matrix of coefficients is singular. From the diagonal form of such a system with only $b_{nn} = 0$, show that it is possible to solve the first $n - 1$ equations for $n - 1$ unknowns in terms of x_n. Apply this analysis to determine non-zero solutions for the systems:

a. $3x_1 + 4x_2 + 5x_3 = 0$
   $6x_1 + 6x_2 + 7x_3 = 0$
   $3x_1 + 8x_2 + 11x_3 = 0.$

b. $x_1 - x_2 + x_3 - x_4 = 0$
   $x_2 - x_4 = 0$
   $x_1 - x_2 - x_3 = 0$
   $x_1 + x_3 - 2x_4 = 0.$

c. $x_1 + 2x_2 - x_3 = 0$
   $x_2 + 2x_3 - x_4 = 0$
   $x_3 + 2x_4 - x_5 = 0$
   $2x_1 - x_3 + x_5 = 0$
   $x_1 + x_2 - 2x_3 + 3x_4 - x_5 = 0.$

2–8. Consider the errors involved in the systems of Exercise 2–5(a) if the constant terms are thought of as the results of a rounding off in the last place given. Indicate the limits of the corresponding solutions.

2–9. Improve the accuracy of the solution of Exercise 2–5(c) by subtracting an earlier approximation for the unknowns and making the corresponding changes in the constant terms, considering the given coefficients to be exact.

2–10. Consider the error involved in the Seidel iteration procedure if the constant terms in a system are in error due to roundoff. Apply this to the systems of Exercise 2–4.

3

Non-linear Equations

3-1. ITERATION METHODS

In many applied problems, the equations involved cannot be written in linear form, and the solution of non-linear equations plays a role in mathematics of importance equal to that of the solution of systems of linear equations. Non-linear methods are usually needed if the terms of the equation are in whole or in part transcendental functions. Some such equations, for example some trigonometric equations, may be reduced to algebraic equations in a variable which represents the value of a particular function. Others, however, combine transcendental with algebraic functions in such a way that no simple separation is possible.

A basic approach to the solution of a non-linear equation involves a set of successive approximations to the precise solution. In some examples several different ways may be considered for setting up an approximation formula. The convergence of the particular scheme chosen must be established, and then the rate of convergence may be speeded up by an appropriate choice of method. If the equation to be solved is reduced to the form

$$x = F(x),$$

a solution is a value of $x = \alpha$ for which $\alpha = F(\alpha)$. In general we will be concerned with only the real roots of these equations. The approximation scheme

$$x_n = F(x_{n-1})$$

produces a sequence $\{x_k\}$ starting with a value x_0 which may be a guess, or the result of another approximation scheme, or merely an arbitrary starting value such as $x_0 = 0$. The convergence of a particular sequence may be tested in terms of the absolute error involved. If $F(x)$ satisfies the condition for the law of the mean, we have the inequality

$$|\alpha - x_k| = |F(\alpha) - F(x_{k-1})| \leq |\alpha - x_{k-1}| \, |F'(z_{k-1})|,$$

where z_k is an appropriate value between α and x_{k-1}. We may write corresponding inequalities for the errors for $k = 1, \ldots, n$. Multiplication of these inequalities and cancellation of repeated terms leads to the inequality,

$$|\alpha - x_n| \leq |\alpha - x_0| \, |F'(z_0)| \, |F'(z_1)| \, \cdots \, |F'(z_{n-1})|.$$

If the set of $F'(z_k)$ for all values of k after some $k = k^*$ is always less than a positive number c less than 1, the sequence of x_n will converge to α in the limit as n becomes infinite. Such a convergence criterion is easy to apply in case $|F'(x)| \leq c < 1$ for all values of x under consideration. A choice between two methods can be made on the basis of such a test. The smaller the later values of $|F'(x_k)|$, the more rapid the convergence will be. For example, consider the equation

$$4 \sin 3x = x^2 + C.$$

For different values of the parameter C this equation has different numbers of roots, or none. This may be shown roughly by inspecting the curves in Fig. 3–1.

For $C = 4$ we see that for no value of x do the curves representing the left side and the right side of the equation intersect, hence there is no real solution of the equation. For $C = 3$ we have two solutions, both positive. For $C = 1$ two additional negative roots arise. For $C = -3$ we see three positive and three negative roots. This set of six roots appears to be the maximum number corresponding to any value of C. The study of the precise limits on C for the different root distributions is itself an example involving the solution of other transcendental equations.

Example 3–1. If we examine the simplest case, $C = 3$, we may write an iteration scheme in several different ways. From

$$4 \sin 3x = x^2 + 3$$

we can write

$$\text{(a)} \quad x = \frac{1}{3} \sin^{-1} \frac{x^2 + 3}{4}$$

or

$$\text{(b)} \quad x = \pm (4 \sin 3x - 3)^{\frac{1}{2}}$$

or

$$\text{(c)} \quad x = \frac{4 \sin 3x - 3}{x}.$$

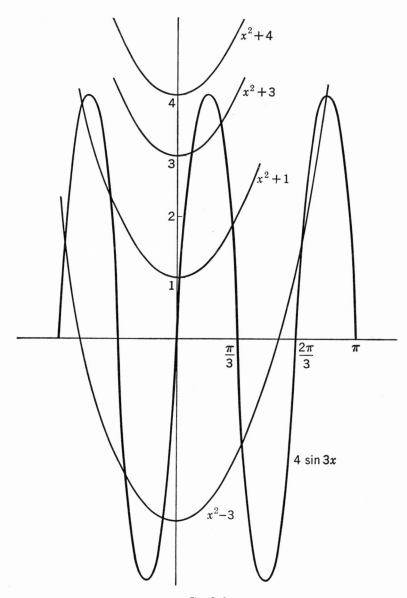

Fig. 3–1

The test for convergence gives, for (a),

$$\left| \frac{1}{6} \frac{x}{\sqrt{1 - [(x^2 + 3)/4]^2}} \right| < 1.$$

The expression $x^2 + 3$ must be no greater than 4 in order that $\sin 3x$ be no larger than 1. We see that the limiting value $x = 1$ makes the derivative $F'(x)$ infinite, while $x = 0$ makes it zero. This suggests that, by starting at an x_0 near zero, convergence might be expected unless the approximate solution get too near $x = 1$.

In formula (b) the derivative is

$$\frac{6 \cos 3x}{(4 \sin 3x - 3)^{\frac{1}{2}}}.$$

Since we see from the diagram that $4 \sin 3x - 3$ is less than 1 in the neighborhood of the roots, we find that $\cos 3x$ must also be small, so here the convergence region includes $x = \pi/6$. We find, however, that the interval about $\pi/6$ is so small that the convergence condition is not satisfied in the neighborhood of either root.

Method (c) results in the test

$$\frac{12x \cos 3x - 4 \sin 3x + 3}{x^2} < 1.$$

Since x is less than 1 in the denominator, while the numerator is less than 1 in absolute value only in a small interval about $\pi/6$, this method will not converge at any point under present consideration.

Let us adopt method (a) with a starting value $x_0 = 0$. Then we have

$$x_1 = \frac{1}{3} \sin^{-1} \frac{3}{4} = \frac{1}{3} (.84) = .28,$$

$$x_2 = \frac{1}{3} \sin^{-1} \frac{3.078}{4} = \frac{1}{3} (.88) = .293,$$

$$x_3 = \frac{1}{3} \sin^{-1} \frac{3.0858}{4} = \frac{1}{3} (.882) = .294.$$

The other root is greater than $\pi/6$. Since the principal value of the inverse sine is no more than $\pi/2$, we must use another branch of the inverse function to converge to this second root. If we start at $x_0 = .5$, we get

$$x_1 = \frac{1}{3} \sin^{-1} \frac{3.25}{4} = \frac{1}{3} \sin^{-1} .81 = \frac{1}{3} (\pi - .95) = \frac{1}{3} (2.19) = .73,$$

$$x_2 = \frac{1}{3} \sin^{-1} \frac{3.533}{4} = \frac{1}{3} \sin^{-1} .883 = \frac{1}{3} (\pi - 1.08) = \frac{1}{3} (2.06) = .69,$$

$$x_3 = \frac{1}{3} \sin^{-1} \frac{3.476}{4} = \frac{1}{3} \sin^{-1} .869 = \frac{1}{3} (\pi - 1.055) = \frac{1}{3} (2.087) = .696.$$

The two roots are approximately $x = .294$ and $x = .696$.

Example 3-2. Let us examine the equation,

$$4 \sin 3x = x^2 - 3.$$

Here $x^2 \leq 7$, hence $-2.65 \leq x \leq 2.65$. The convergence condition for method (a) gives

$$\frac{1}{6} \frac{|x|}{\sqrt{1 - [(x^2 - 3)/4]^2}} < 1,$$

and we see again that the derivative becomes infinite as x^2 approaches 7. We may reduce the above condition to a simpler algebraic form,

$$9x^4 - 50x^2 - 63 < 0,$$

and here

$$x^2 < 6.6.$$

Thus we again may use method (a) to approximate all the six roots indicated in the diagram, except the one beyond $5\pi/6$, by choosing the correct branch of the inverse sine.

For method (b) in this instance the condition is

$$\left| \frac{6 \cos 3x}{(4 \sin 3x + 3)^{\frac{1}{2}}} \right| < 1.$$

We find this condition is satisfied at $x = 5\pi/6$, and also in the interval about $5\pi/6$ in which $\sin 3x > .9$, which includes the neighborhood of the largest root. Let us start at $x_0 = 5\pi/6$:

$$x_1 = (4 + 3)^{\frac{1}{2}} = 2.65,$$
$$x_2 = (4 \sin 7.95 + 3)^{\frac{1}{2}} = (6.980)^{\frac{1}{2}} = 2.64.$$

If we apply this formula to the negative root near $-\frac{2}{3}$ we have

$$x_1 = -3^{\frac{1}{2}} = -1.7,$$
$$x_2 = -4 \sin (-5.1) + 3^{\frac{1}{2}} = -(6.7)^{\frac{1}{2}} = -2.8,$$

and this diverges.

3-2. GEOMETRIC METHODS

One type of iteration procedure is based on formulas of the general form,

$$(3\text{-}1) \qquad\qquad x_{k+1} = x_k - \frac{f(x_k)}{\beta_k}$$

which is obviously satisfied at a root $x = \alpha$ for any set of β_k in the form

$$\alpha = \alpha - \frac{0}{\beta_k}.$$

Geometric considerations usually determine an appropriate choice of β_k. If the signs of $f(x_k)$ and $f(x_{k-1})$ are different, the choice

$$\beta_k = \frac{f(x_k) - f(x_{k-1})}{x_k - x_{k-1}}$$

corresponds geometrically to using the slope of the line through these points of the graph of $f(x)$. Then Eq. (3-1) makes x_{k+1} the x-intercept of this line. This is the method, historically called *regula falsi*, or more descriptively the method of linear interpolation. It is illustrated in Fig. 3-2.

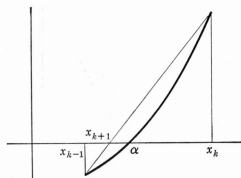

Fig. 3-2

Example 3-3.　For example, in the solution of the equation

$$f(x) = xe^{2x} - 4x - 2 = 0,$$

we find $f(0) = -2$ and $f(1) = e^2 - 6 = 1.39$. Since these are of opposite signs, a root lies between $x = 0$ and $x = 1$. Then

$$\beta_1 = e^2 - 4$$

and

$$x_2 = 1 - \frac{e^2 - 6}{e^2 - 4} = \frac{2}{e^2 - 4}$$

$$= \frac{2}{3.39} = .6.$$

Then

$$f(.6) = (.6)3.32 - 4.4 = -2.41,$$

$$\beta_2 = \frac{-2.41 - 1.39}{.6 - 1} = 9.5,$$

$$x_3 = .6 + \frac{2.41}{9.5} = .85,$$

$$f(.85) = (.85)(5.47) - 5.4 = .75.$$

This method is relatively slow in its convergence.

A method, due to Newton, and usually called the Newton-Raphson method, makes β_k the slope of the tangent to the graph of $f(x)$ at x_k. This gives the form

$$x_{k+1} = x_k - \frac{f(x_k)}{f'(x_k)}.$$

The geometry of this method is shown in Fig. 3-3.

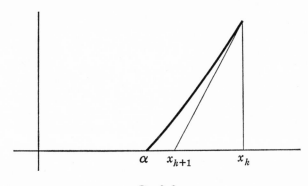

Fig. 3-3

Example 3-4. If we apply this method to the example

$$xe^{2x} - 4x - 2 = 0,$$

we have

$$f'(x) = 2xe^{2x} + e^{2x} - 4,$$
$$f(1) = 1.39,$$
$$f'(1) = 18.2$$
$$x_2 = 1 - \frac{1.39}{18.2} = .94$$
$$f(.94) = .94(6.554) - 5.76 = .29$$
$$f'(.94) = 2.88(6.554) - 4 = 14.8$$
$$x_3 = .94 - \frac{.29}{14.8} = .92$$
$$f(.92) = .92(6.30) - 5.680 = .120.$$

This method usually converges to the root more rapidly than that of linear interpolation.

In some problems a more or less arbitrary choice of β_k may lead to a convergent set of approximations, for example it may be convenient to choose an unvarying value of β_k rather than one depending on k. Since the slope of the tangent changes only slightly in the neighborhood of a root, we might choose β_k as a convenient constant value near this slope.

In the example above let us set $\beta_k = 15$.   Then

$$f(.92) = .92(6.30) - 5.68 = .12$$
$$x_2 = .92 - \frac{.12}{15} = .912$$
$$f(.912) = .912(6.19) - 5.67 = -.020$$
$$x_3 = .912 + \frac{.020}{15} = .9133.$$

The convenience of calculating only $f(x_k)$ may make up for possibly slower convergence.

3-3. RATE OF CONVERGENCE

The rate at which convergence of these iteration procedures takes place may be studied by applying the law of the mean to $f(x)$.   We write

$$x_{k+1} = x_k - \frac{f(x_k)}{\beta_k}.$$

If α is a root of the equation $f(x) = 0$, we set up the form

$$\alpha - x_{k+1} = \alpha - x_k - \frac{f(\alpha) - f(x_k)}{\beta_k} = \alpha - x_k - \frac{(\alpha - x_k)f'(z_k)}{\beta_k}$$

where z_k is a value between α and x_k.   Here the error in x_{k+1} is related to the error in x_k by the formula

$$|\alpha - x_{k+1}| \leq |\alpha - x_k| \left| 1 - \frac{f'(z_k)}{\beta_k} \right|.$$

In Newton's method, β_k is chosen as the value of $f'(x)$ at x_k.   By extending the law of the mean one more term, we can write for Newton's method

$$\alpha - x_{k+1} = \alpha - x_k - \frac{(\alpha - x_k)f'(x_k) + (\alpha - x_k)^2 f''(z_k)}{f'(x_k)}$$
$$= -(\alpha - x_k)^2 \frac{f''(z_k)}{f'(x_k)}.$$

Hence this choice of β_k makes the error in x_{k+1} proportional to the square of the error in x_k.   When the latter error is reduced to the order of 10^{-n}, use of Newton's method may increase the precision n more decimal places.   This holds only for n greater than some n_0 which depends on the individual case.

Example 3-5. For example, let us solve the equation

$$e^x = 4x^2.$$

The root between 0 and 1 may be approximated by Newton's method

$$x_1 = 1 - \frac{e^1 - 4}{e^1 - 8} = \frac{4}{8 - e} = .8,$$

$$x_2 = .8 - \frac{e^{.8} - 2.56}{e^{.8} - 6.4} = .75,$$

$$x_3 = .75 - \frac{e^{.75} - 2.25}{e^{.75} - 6} = .71,$$

$$x_4 = .71 - \frac{e^{.71} - 2.016}{e^{.71} - 5.68} = .7150.$$

If we consider the same root from the equation $e^{x/2} = 2x$, Newton's method gives

$$x_1 = 1 - \frac{e^{.5} - 2}{\frac{1}{2}e^{.5} - 2} = .7,$$

$$x_2 = .7 - \frac{e^{.35} - 1.4}{\frac{1}{2}e^{.35} - 2} = .715,$$

$$x_3 = .715 - \frac{e^{.357} - 1.43}{\frac{1}{2}e^{.357} - 2} = .7148.$$

The second form of this solution converges more rapidly because of the relative size of the factor $f''(x)/f'(x)$ in the two cases. Since we are working for one root at a time, different forms might be the more appropriate for different roots of the same equation.

One advantage of Newton's method over some other iterative method of this chapter, is the fact that computation of a new approximation uses only functions involved in the original equation, so that rough estimates or even possible errors will not interfere with the ultimate accuracy of a computation.

3-4. APPROXIMATION FORMULAS

Newton's method may be used to derive formulas for simple approximations to square roots and reciprocals which are useful with computing systems of limited ability. For example, an approximation method for the square root of a number may be written by applying Newton's formula to the equation

$$f(x) = x^2 - N = 0.$$

Here,

$$f'(x) = 2x,$$

$$x_{n+1} = x_n - \frac{x_n^2 - N}{2x_n} = \frac{1}{2}\left(x_n + \frac{N}{x_n}\right).$$

Another form comes from writing

$$f(x) = x - \frac{N}{x} = 0.$$

Then,

$$f'(x) = 1 + \frac{N}{x^2}$$

$$x_{n+1} = x_n - \frac{x_n - N/x_n}{1 + N/x_n^2} = \frac{2x_nN}{x_n^2 + N} = \frac{N}{\frac{1}{2}(x_n + N/x_n)}.$$

A third form is derived from

$$f(x) = 1 - \frac{N}{x^2}.$$

In this case,

$$f'(x) = \frac{2N}{x^3}$$

$$x_{n+1} = x_n - \frac{1 - N/x_n^2}{2N/x_n^3} = \frac{x_n(3N - x_n^2)}{2N} = x_n\left(\frac{3}{2} - \frac{x_n^2}{2N}\right).$$

Example 3–6. Let us apply these formulas to the computation of $\sqrt{10}$. We take in the first form

$$x_1 = 3;$$

then

$$x_2 = \tfrac{1}{2}(3 + \tfrac{10}{3}) = 3.16,$$

and

$$x_3 = \frac{1}{2}\left(3.16 + \frac{10}{3.16}\right) = 3.1623.$$

By the second form,

$$x_2 = \frac{2(3)10}{9 + 10} = 3.15,$$

$$x_3 = \frac{2(3.15)10}{9.9 + 10} = 3.166;$$

and by the third,

$$x_2 = \frac{3(30 - 9)}{20} = 3.15,$$

$$x_3 = \frac{3.15(30 - 9.92)}{20} = 3.1626.$$

Let us compare the rates of convergence of these three methods. We derived the relation

$$\alpha - x_{k+1} = -(\alpha - x_k)^2 \frac{f''(z_k)}{f'(x_k)}.$$

In comparing the three forms, we evaluate the factor f''/f' at the approximation to the root:

(a) $\dfrac{f''}{f'} = \dfrac{2}{2x} = \dfrac{1}{x}.$

(b) $\dfrac{f''}{f'} = -\dfrac{2N}{x^3} \bigg/ \left(1 + \dfrac{N}{x^2}\right) = \dfrac{-2N}{x^3 + Nx}.$

(c) $\dfrac{f''}{f'} = \dfrac{-6N}{x^4} \bigg/ \dfrac{2N}{x^3} = -\dfrac{3}{x}.$

In Example 3–6, the values of these factors are

(a) $\dfrac{1}{3},\qquad \dfrac{1}{3.15}.$

(b) $-\dfrac{20}{57},\quad -\dfrac{20}{61.25}.$

(c) $-1,\quad -\dfrac{3}{3.15}.$

We would expect the first form to converge most rapidly when $x^2 < N$.

A corresponding formula for the reciprocal of N can be obtained from the equation

$$f(x) = N - \frac{1}{x} = 0.$$

Here,

$$f'(x) = \frac{1}{x^2}$$

$$x_{n+1} = x_n - \frac{N - 1/x_n}{1/x_n^2} = x_n(2 - Nx_n).$$

This achieves division by multiplication.

Example 3–7. For example, if $N = 12$, take $x_1 = .1$; then

$$x_2 = .1(2 - 1.2) = .08,$$
$$x_3 = .08(2 - .96) = .0832,$$
$$x_4 = .0832(2 - .9984) = .08333312.$$

EXERCISES

3–1. Approximate the roots of the following equations to three places of decimals:

a. $4 \sin 3x = x^2 + 2.$
b. $4 \sin 3x = x^2 + 1.$
c. $4 \sin 3x = x^2 - 3.$
d. $e^{2x} = x^2 - 4.$
e. $e^x = x^3 - x.$

3-2. Test different possible iteration methods for convergence in the following equations:

  a. $x^2 \sin 2x = 3$.
  b. $x^3 \ln (1 + x) = 2$.
  c. $\ln (1 + x) = x^2 - 4x - 4$.

3-3. Use iterative methods to approximate the following roots to 6 significant places:

  a. $\sqrt{79}$.
  b. $\sqrt{156342}$.
  c. $\sqrt{.0136754}$.

3-4. Develop a simple formula for approximating the solution of the following functional equations by using Newton's method. Use the value $N = \frac{1}{3}$, and approximate a corresponding root to three decimal places.

  a. $x^3 - N = 0$.

  b. $\dfrac{N}{x^3} - 1 = 0$.

  c. $\sin x - N = 0, N < 1$.
  d. $e^x - N = 0, N > 0$.

3-5. a. Compare the rates of convergence of the formulas derived in Exercise 3-4 (a), (b).
     b. Obtain another formula for cube root with optimum convergence rate.

3-6. Determine the limiting values of C in the equation $4 \sin 3x = x^2 + C$ for which the equation has double roots. Use these values to indicate the number of roots of the equation as a function of the variable C.

4

Polynomial Equations

4-1. ROOTS OF POLYNOMIAL EQUATIONS

Problems involving the roots of polynomial equations occur more frequently than those involving transcendental functions, and methods of solution have been developed that are adapted to properties of polynomials. Of course, the methods studied in the previous chapter may be used, and in some cases iterative methods converge very rapidly. Formulas giving the roots of a polynomial equation in terms of powers and roots of the coefficients of the terms in the polynomial are available for third- and fourth-degree equations. These forms, however, usually must be reduced to approximate numbers at some point in their applications, and in many cases a direct approach to this approximate root is more useful. We will confine our attention to polynomials with real coefficients.

4-2. SYNTHETIC SUBSTITUTION

Verification that a particular number is a root of an equation involves the substitution of a value of the variable which reduces the equation to an identity. In the form $P_n(x) = 0$, where $P_n(x) = a_0 x^n + a_1 x^{n-1} + \cdots + a_{n-1}x + a_n$, it is possible to rearrange the steps in the substitution so that a succession of multiplications and additions replaces the calculation of high powers of the substituted value. If r is to be substituted for x in $P_n(x)$, we may set up the form

(4-1)

a_0	a_1	a_2	$\cdots$	a_n	r
	$b_0 r$	$b_1 r$		$b_{n-1}r$	
$b_0 = a_0$	$b_1 = b_0 r + a_1$	$b_2 = b_1 r + a_2$	$\cdots$	$R = b_n = b_{n-1}r + a_n.$	

We may also write the polynomial in the form

$$P_n(x) = (x - r)Q_{n-1}(x) + R$$

thus:

$$
\begin{aligned}
P_n(x) &= (b_0 x^{n-1} + b_1 x^{n-2} + \cdots + b_{n-1})(x - r) + R \\
&= b_0 x^n + (b_1 - r b_0)x^{n-1} + \cdots + (b_k - r b_{k-1})x^{n-k} + \cdots \\
&\qquad\qquad\qquad\qquad\qquad\qquad\qquad\qquad + R - r b_{n-1} \\
&= a_0 x^n + a_1 x^{n-1} + \cdots + a_n.
\end{aligned}
$$

The coefficients b_k are the intermediate numbers generated in the synthetic substitution procedure, and the remainder R is evidently the value of $P_n(r)$. If R is zero, r is a zero of the polynomial, and $Q_{n-1}(x)$ is the quotient when $P_n(x)$ is divided by $x - r$. Hence $Q_{n-1}(x)$ is the polynomial whose zeroes are the other roots of the equation, and the procedure may be repeated for all n zeroes of $P_n(x)$ with the degree of the polynomial reduced at each step. This format, Eq. (4-1) is called synthetic substitution, or sometimes synthetic division because of the resemblance to division by $x - r$. The steps involved in this substitution may be accumulated on a desk computer in such a manner that no intermediate values need to be written. An electronic computer also is adapted to forming this sort of result. The major error in polynomials of high degree is roundoff since only a limited number of places may be carried on the machine. It is possible by this method to check directly on the value of the polynomial for a succession of values $r^{(k)}$ such that $P_n(r^{(k)})$ is reduced to as near zero as the machine calculation will permit. This is essentially an inverse interpolation for the value of x which makes $P_n(x)$ exactly zero.

If there are any rational roots of a polynomial equation with integer coefficients, we will prove that the numerators of these roots are integer factors of the constant term a_n and the denominators are integer factors of a_0. Write the rational root in the form $r = p/q$, where p and q are integers with no common factors. Then

$$a_0\left(\frac{p}{q}\right)^n + a_1\left(\frac{p}{q}\right)^{n-1} + \cdots + a_{n-1}\left(\frac{p}{q}\right) + a_n = 0.$$

Hence

$$a_0\frac{p^n}{q} = -(a_1 p^{n-1} + a_2 p^{n-2}q + \cdots + a_n q^{n-1}).$$

Since the right side is made up entirely of products and sums of integers, the left side must be an integer also, and therefore q must be a factor of a_0.   Similarly

$$a_n \frac{q^n}{p} = -(a_{n-1}q^{n-1} + a_{n-2}q^{n-2}p + \cdots + a_0p^{n-1}),$$

and therefore p must be a factor of a_n.

By means of this theorem, any rational roots of polynomial equations of this type may be discovered by checking all possible ratios of the factors of a_0 and a_n.   When the factors involving these roots are removed, the polynomial equation of lowest degree with only irrational and complex roots may be investigated by other methods.

Example 4-1.   To find the rational roots of $8x^4 - 28x^3 + 6x^2 + 31x + 10 = 0$, we consider the factors 1, 2, 4, 8 of a_0 and 1, 2, 5, 10 of a_4 and their negatives. Of the 32 possible ratios only 20 different rational numbers in lowest terms remain, and among them only 2, $\frac{5}{2}$, and $-\frac{1}{2}$ are roots, the latter a double root.

Example 4-2.   For the equation

$$P_3(x) = x^3 + 3x - 5 = 0,$$

$P_3(2) = 9$ and $P_3(1) = -1$.   Hence there is a root between 1 and 2, probably nearer 1:

1	0	3	-5	1.1
	1.1	1.21	4.631	
1	1.1	4.21	$-.369$	

1	0	3	-5	1.16
	1.16	1.3456	5.040896	
1	1.16	4.3456	.040896	

Complex roots as well as real roots may be located in this way, although the algebra of the complex numbers makes this method more difficult.   The main decision in such procedures is to choose a value of $r^{(k+1)}$ which will cut down on the absolute value of the remainder, compared to that for $r^{(k)}$.

A method, called Lin's method, uses the recursion formula

$$(4\text{--}2) \qquad\qquad r^{(k+1)} = r^{(k)} - \frac{R^{(k)}}{b_{n-1}^{(k)}}.$$

This is based on the step in which $R = b_{n-1}r + a_n = P_n(r)$.   Now if $P_n(r + h) = 0$, we have, for an appropriate b_{n-1},

$$0 = b_{n-1}(r + h) + a_n$$
$$r + h = -\frac{a_n}{b_{n-1}}.$$

If we set $r + h = r^{(k+1)}$ and use the b_{n-1} already calculated, we have the approximation

$$r^{(k+1)} - r^{(k)} = -\frac{a_n}{b_{n-1}^{(k)}} - r^{(k)} = -\frac{R^{(k)}}{b_{n-1}^{(k)}}.$$

This choice corresponds to writing the equation to be solved in the iteration form,

$$(4\text{--}3) \qquad\qquad x = \frac{x a_n}{a_n - P_n(x)}.$$

The convergence condition on the derivative of the right side is

$$(4\text{--}4) \qquad\qquad \left| \frac{a_n[a_n - P_n(x) + xP'_n(x)]}{[P_n(x) - a_n]^2} \right| < 1.$$

At a root $x = \alpha$ we have, for convergence,

$$(4\text{--}5) \qquad\qquad \left| 1 + \frac{\alpha P'(\alpha)}{a_n} \right| < 1.$$

This condition is difficult to satisfy in many cases with large roots. Some approximate roots satisfy the convergence condition in approaching the root from one side only. The derivative $P'(x)$ may also be evaluated by synthetic methods. By differentiating the relation

$$P_n(x) = (x - r)Q_{n-1}(x) + R,$$

we have

$$P'_n(x) = Q'_{n-1}(x)(x - r) + Q_{n-1}(x).$$

Hence we find that $P'_n(r) = Q_{n-1}(r)$ is the remainder R' when $Q_{n-1}(x)$ is divided by $x - r$. This may be written in the previous synthetic form by repeating the process on the $b_0, \ldots, b_{n-1}$ coefficients:

$(4\text{--}6)$

b_0	b_1	b_r	$\ldots$	b_{n-1}	r
	$c_0 r$	$c_{n-1} r$		$c_{n-2} r$	
$c_0 = b_0$	$c_1 = c_0 r + b_1$	$c_k = c_{k-1} r + b_k$	$\ldots$	$R' = c_n = c_{n-1} r + b_{n-1}.$	

Similar operations on the c_k gives a remainder R'' which is equivalent to $P''_n(r)/2$. This follows because we may write

$$P_n(x) = (x - r)^2 Q_{n-2}(x) + Rx + S,$$
$$P''_n(x) = 2Q_{n-2}(x) + (x - r)^2 Q''_{n-2}(x) + 2(x - r)Q'_{n-2}(x),$$
$$P''_n(r) = 2Q_{n-2}(r) = 2R''.$$

Example 4–3. For the equation

$$P_4(x) = x^4 - 6x^3 + 2x^2 - 8x + 10 = 0,$$

$P_4(0) = 10$, $P_4(1) = -1$, $P_4(5) = -105$, $P_4(6) = 34$, so there are roots between 0 and 1, and between 5 and 6. Let us approximate the former:

$$
\begin{array}{rrrrrr}
1 & -6 & 2 & -8 & 10 & 1 \\
  & 1 & -5 & -3 & -11 & \\
\hline
1 & -5 & -3 & -11 & -1 & \\
  & 1 & -4 & -7 & & \\
\hline
1 & -4 & -7 & -18. & & \\
\end{array}
$$

Here b_{n-1} is -11, R is -1, and R' is -18. The convergence condition is satisfied in the approximation

$$\left| 1 - \frac{18}{10} \right| < 1.$$

Our second approximation is

$$r^{(2)} = 1 - \frac{1}{11} = .9.$$

Then

$$
\begin{array}{rrrrrr}
1 & -6 & 2 & -8 & 10 & .9 \\
  & .9 & -4.59 & -2.331 & -9.2979 & \\
\hline
1 & -5.1 & -2.59 & -10.331 & .7021 & \\
\end{array}
$$

$$r^{(3)} = .9 + \frac{.702}{10.33} = .97$$

$$
\begin{array}{rrrrrr}
1 & -6 & 2 & -8 & 10 & .97 \\
  & .97 & -4.879 & -2.7926 & -10.4688 & \\
\hline
1 & -5.03 & -2.879 & -10.7926 & -.4688 & \\
\end{array}
$$

$$r^{(4)} = .97 - \frac{.4688}{10.79} = .927$$

$$
\begin{array}{rrrrrr}
1 & -6 & 2 & -8 & 10 & .93 \\
  & .93 & -4.715 & -2.5250 & -9.7883 & \\
\hline
1 & -5.93 & -2.715 & -10.5250 & .2117 & \\
\end{array}
$$

$$r^{(5)} = .93 + \frac{.2117}{10.5} = .95$$

$$
\begin{array}{rrrrrr}
1 & -6 & 2 & -8 & 10 & .95 \\
  & .95 & -4.7975 & -2.6576 & -10.1247 & \\
\hline
1 & -5.05 & -2.7975 & -10.6576 & -.1247 & \\
\end{array}
$$

$$r^{(6)} = .95 - \frac{.1247}{10.66} = .94$$

$$
\begin{array}{rrrrrr}
1 & -6 & 2 & -8 & 10 & .94 \\
  & .94 & -4.7564 & -2.591 & -9.9555 & \\
\hline
1 & -5.06 & -2.7564 & -10.591 & .0445 & \\
\end{array}
$$

$$r^{(7)} = .94 + \frac{.0445}{10.591} = .944.$$

4-3. NEWTON'S METHOD

The same synthetic technique may be used to calculate the numbers R and R' used in the Newton-Raphson approximation of Art. 3-3:

$$r^{(k+1)} = r^{(k)} - \frac{R}{R'}.$$

Example 4-4.   In the equation

$$P_4(x) = x^4 + 2x^3 + 3x^2 + 2x - 4 = 0,$$

we observe that one root lies between 0 and 1.

Synthetic methods give

1	2	3	2	−4	1
	1	3	6	8	
1	3	6	8	4 = R	
	1	4	10		
1	4	10	18 = R'		

$$r^{(2)} = 1 - \frac{4}{18} = .8\ldots$$

1	2	3	2	−4	.8
	.8		4.192	4.9536	
1	2.8	5.24	6.192	.9536	
	.8	2.88	6.496		
1	3.6	8.12	12.688		

$$r^{(3)} = .8 - \frac{.95}{12.7} = .7\ldots.$$

Obviously it is useless to calculate R and R' to five places with only a one-place approximation for r.   We need many-digit calculations only when differences between nearly equal numbers are involved.   We proceed as follows:

1	2	3	2	−4	.7
	.7	1.89	3.423	3.7961	
1	2.7	4.89	5.423	−.2039	
	.7	2.38	5.089		
1	3.4	7.27	10.512		
	.7	2.87			
1	4.1	10.14			

$$r^{(4)} = .7 + .02$$

1	2	3	2	−4	.72
	.72	1.9584	3.570	4.0104	
1	2.72	4.9584	5.570	.0104.	

Since the value of R' for $r = .72$ must lie between 10.5 and 12.7, we see that a next approximation to r will be $r^{(5)} = .719$. By continuing this process we may approximate r to as many places as we choose to carry out the multiplications. With a desk calculator this is a matter of a few minutes, and with a larger computer it may be a few milliseconds. As we determined in Art. 3–3, the convergence criterion in the Newton-Raphson method is

$$\left| \frac{P_n P_n''}{(P_n')^2} \right| < 1.$$

In this example we have, at $r^{(4)}$,

$$\frac{2(.2038)(10.14)}{(10.5)^2} = .04 < 1.$$

We may also use the Newton-Raphson method for the determination of a complex root, but in this case we must use a complex value of r as an approximation. Then R and R' usually are also complex numbers, but the approximation formula

$$r_{k+1} = r_k - \frac{R}{R'}$$

can be used. The measure of the error involved is the relatively small absolute value of R/R'.

Example 4–5. The equation

$$x^3 + 2x^2 + x - 1 = 0$$

has a real root between 1 and 0. However, to illustrate the procedures, if we substitute $r^{(1)} = -1 + i$, we get

1	2	1	-1	$-1 + i$
	$-1 + i$	-2	$1 - i$	
1	$1 + i$	-1	$- i$	
	$-1 + i$	$-2 - 2i$		
2	$2i$	$-3 - 2i$		

$$r^{(2)} = -1 + i - \frac{i}{3 + 2i} = -1.2 + .8i$$

1	2	1	-1	$-1.2 + .8i$
	$-1.2 + .8i$	$-1.6 - .32i$	$.976 - .096i$	
1	$.8 + .8i$	$-.6 - .32i$	$-.024 - .096i$	
	$-1.2 + .8i$	$-.8 - 2.24i$		
1	$-.4 + 1.6i$	$-1.4 - 2.56i$		

$$r^{(3)} = -1.2 + .8i - \frac{-.024 - .096i}{-1.4 - 2.56i} \cong -1.23 + .78i.$$

Clearly, the root is close to $r^{(3)}$. Of course, the complex conjugate of this number is also a root. The pair of factors corresponding to these roots forms a polynomial of the form

$$[x - (-1.23 + .78i)][x - (-1.23 - .78i)] = x^2 + 2.46x + 2.12.$$

4–4. COMPLEX ROOT PAIRS

The difficult problem of locating roots of fourth- or sixth-degree equations with no real roots may be approached by attempting to find the quadratic factors corresponding to pairs of complex roots. The polynomial

$$P_n(x) = x^n + a_1x^{n-1} + \cdots + a_n$$

may be factored:

$$(x^2 + px + q)(x^{n-2} + b_1x^{n-3} + \cdots + b_{n-2}) + Rx + S.$$

By multiplying and comparing coefficients we find the equations

$$b_1 = a_1 - p, \quad b_2 = a_2 - pb_1 - q, \quad \ldots, \quad b_k = a_k - pb_{k-1} - qb_{k-2},$$
$$R = b_{n-1} = a_{n-1} - pb_{n-2} - qb_{b-3},$$
$$S = b_n + pb_{n-1} = a_n - qb_{n-2}.$$

The reduction of the coefficients R and S in the remainder $Rx + S$ to near-zero values is the test of the closeness of the approximation of the trial polynomial

$$x^2 + px + q$$

to the factor corresponding to a pair of complex roots. If one choice of p and q leads to a set of b_k, Lin's method involves the use of the equations

$$q^* = \frac{a_n}{b_{n-2}},$$
$$p^* = \frac{a_{n-1} - qb_{n-3}}{b_{n-2}},$$

obtained by setting the expressions for R and S equal to zero. These lead to iteration formulas of the form

$$p^* = p + \frac{R}{b_{n-2}},$$
$$q^* = q + \frac{S}{b_{n-2}}.$$

A synthetic arrangement of the a_n and b_n can be set up much like that used for single roots. This form may be written as follows:

$$
\begin{array}{llll}
1 & a_1 & a_2 & a_3 & \ldots \\
 & & -pb_1 & -pb_2 & \\
 & -p & -q & -qb_1 & \\
\hline
1 & b_1 = a_1 - p & b_2 = a_2 - pb_1 - q & b_3 = a_3 - pb_2 - qb_1 & \ldots
\end{array}
$$

$$
\begin{array}{llll}
 & a_{n-1} & a_n & & 1 \quad p \quad q \\
 & -pb_{n-2} & & & \\
 & -qb_{n-3} & -qb_{n-2} & & \\
\hline
 & R = a_{n-1} - pb_{n-2} - qb_{n-3} & S = a_n - qb_{n-2} & &
\end{array}
$$

Example 4-6. Let us solve the equation $x^4 + 12x^3 + 48x^2 + 72x + 52 = 0$. We choose the initial values of p and q by ignoring the terms in x^4 and x^3 and approximating the quadratic factor by $x^2 + 1.5x + 1$. Long division by this factor would be written

$$
\begin{array}{ll}
x^4 + 12x^3 + 48x^2 + 72x + 52(& x^2 + 1.5x + 1 \\
x^4 + 1.5x^3 + x^2 & \\
\cline{1-1}
\quad 10.5x^3 + 47x^2 & x^2 + 10.5x + 31.25 \\
\quad 10.5x^3 + 15.75x^2 + 10.5x & \\
\cline{1-1}
\qquad\quad 31.25x^2 + 61.5x & \\
\qquad\quad 31.25x^2 + 46.875x + 31.25 & \\
\cline{1-1}
\qquad\qquad\quad + 15.625x + 20.75. &
\end{array}
$$

The essential numbers of this display correspond to the b_k, R, and S of the previous factorization scheme. By changing the signs of p and q, we may change the subtraction in the long division to addition in the synthetic form and thus write all essential terms as follows:

1	12	48	72	52	1	1.5	1
		−15.75	−46.875				
	−1.5	−1	−10.5	−31.25			
1	10.5	31.25	15.625	20.75			
	b_1	b_2	R	S			

Lin's method gives $p^* - p = \Delta p$ and $q^* - q = \Delta q$ as $\Delta p = R/b_2 = .5$ and $\Delta q = S/b_2 = .6$. A second factorization gives

1	12	48	72	52	1	2	1.6
		−20	−52.8				
	−2	−1.6	−16	−42.24			
	10	26.4	3.2	9.76			

$$\Delta p = .1, \quad \Delta q = .3$$

1	12	48	72	52	1	2.1	1.9
		−19.89	−55.041				
	−2.1	−1.9	−18.91	−49.799			
	9.9	26.21	−1.951	2.201			

$$\Delta p = -.1, \quad \Delta q = .1$$

1	12	48	72	52	1	2	2
		−20	−52				
	−2	−2	−20	−52			
	10	26	0	0.			

The factors are $x^2 + 2x + 2$ and $x^2 + 10x + 26$. They determine the roots to be $-1 \pm i$ and $-5 \pm i$.

The relatively large ratio of the absolute values of the two pairs of roots in Example 4–6 helps to speed the convergence of Lin's method. Other methods involving similar factorization are used for the determination of complex root pairs.[H2]

EXERCISES

4–1. Approximate a real root of the following equations to three decimal places:

a. $x^3 - 0.5x^2 - 0.4x - 1.5 = 0$.
b. $x^3 - 5x^2 + 11x - 60 = 0$.
c. $x^3 + x^2 + x - 4 = 0$.
d. $2x^3 - 5x^2 - 2x - 4 = 0$.
e. $9x^3 - 8x^2 - 7x - 5 = 0$.

4–2. Use Lin's method to approximate all real roots of the following equations to four decimals:

a. $x^3 - 3x^2 + 3 = 0$.
b. $x^4 - .3x^3 + .2x^2 + .3x - 1 = 0$.
c. $10x^4 + 7x^3 - 2x^2 - 5x - 14 = 0$.

4–3. Use Newton's method to approximate the real roots of the following equations to four decimals:

a. $x^3 - 4.2x^2 + 3 = 0$.
b. $x^4 + x^3 - 2x^2 - 3x - 3 = 0$.
c. $10x^4 + 4x^3 - 3x^2 - 2x - 15 = 0$.
d. $5x^4 - 3x^3 + 12x^2 - 7x + 10 = 0$.
e. $x^4 - .25x^3 + .36x^2 - .13x + .74 = 0$.

4–4. Show that Lin's method converges at only one of the roots of the equation

$$x^3 - 3x^2 + 3 = 0,$$

while Newton's method converges at all three roots. Approximate these roots to three decimals.

4–5. Use the Newton-Raphson method to approximate the complex roots of the equation

$$x^4 + 6x^3 + 18x^2 + 28x + 24 = 0.$$

The real parts of the roots are negative.

4-6. Use Lin's quadratic factor method to approximate the complex roots of the equations:

a. $x^4 + 2x^3 + 7x^2 + 8x + 16 = 0$.
b. $x^4 + 2x^3 + 6x^2 - 13x + 48 = 0$.

4-7. Use substitutions to reduce the following equations to polynomial form, solve for approximate roots of these equations, and then find corresponding solutions to the original equations:

a. $\cos^3 x - .123 \cos^2 x + .145 \cos x - .345 = 0$.
b. $e^{4x} - 2e^{2x} - 5e^x + 7 = 0$.
c. $\tan^4 x - \tan^2 x - 2 \tan x - 1 = 0$.

4-8. Reduce the following polynomial equations to equations of lower degree before approximating the roots to such a point that the real roots of the original equations are approximated to three decimals:

a. $x^9 - 3x^3 - 5 = 0$.
b. $4x^6 - 7x^4 + 5x^2 - 9 = 0$.
c. $3x^{12} - 2x^9 + 3x^6 - 2x^3 - 5 = 0$.

4-9. The characteristic values of a matrix A are defined as the numbers λ that satisfy the matrix equation

$$Ax = \lambda x \text{ or } (A - \lambda I)x = 0,$$

where λ is an appropriate characteristic vector. These values are obtained as roots of the equation formed by setting the determinant of the matrix $A - \lambda I$ equal to zero. Determine the characteristic values and vectors for the following matrices:

a. $\begin{pmatrix} 1 & 1 & 0 \\ 1 & 2 & 1 \\ 0 & 1 & 3 \end{pmatrix}$.

b. $\begin{pmatrix} 4 & 1 & 1 \\ 2 & 6 & 3 \\ 1 & 2 & 8 \end{pmatrix}$.

4-10. In polynomial equations it is possible to approximate the real roots of largest absolute value or of smallest absolute value by iterative methods in the form

$$x = -\frac{a_1 + a_2 x^{-1} + a_3 x^{-2} + \cdots + a_n x^{-n+1}}{a_0}$$

or

$$x = -\frac{a_n + a_{n-2} x^2 + \cdots + a_0 x^n}{a_{n-1}}.$$

Use these methods to approximate roots of the following equations:

a. $x^5 + 15x^4 - 6x^3 - 3x^2 + 10x - 2 = 0$.
b. $x^8 + 4x^7 - 2x^5 - 3x^4 - 5x - 1 = 0$.
c. $x^6 + 2.35x^5 - .723x^4 - .547x^3 + .394x^2 - 4.63x + 1.36 = 0$.

5

Numerical Integration

5-1. INTEGRATION

Numerical methods of integration may be used when the integrand involved is a function for which no convenient indefinite integral is available. They may also be used when the only information about the integrand comes from discrete tabular values. This latter condition arises especially in the numerical solution of a differential equation. Sometimes the repeated use of a simple numerical integration (quadrature) formula involving many steps is appropriate, especially if a computer is available for the routine calculations. In other cases, more complicated formulas may be used, involving some arbitrary decisions on the part of the user, when these formulas have higher precision and hence involve fewer repetitions of the operations.

5-2. NEWTON-COATES FORMULAS

All numerical methods of integration are based on representing the value of a definite integral in terms of the value of the integrand, or of its derivatives, at various points of the interval of integration. The simplest examples are the major and minor sums used in the definition of the Riemann integral. For $f(x)$ on the interval (a, b),

$$\underline{J} = \underline{f_1}\Delta x_1 + \cdots + \underline{f_n}\Delta x_n \leq \int_a^b f(x) \, dx \leq \bar{f_1}\Delta x_1 + \cdots + \bar{f_n}\Delta x_n = \bar{J}$$

where $\{\Delta x_i\}$ represent a partition of the interval (a, b) into n subintervals, and x_i is a point in Δx_i. The lower bar indicates the minimum value of $f(x_i)$, and the upper bar the maximum value on the interval Δx_i. Then the approximate evaluation of the integral by either $\underline{J}$ or $\bar{J}$ usually involves an error that decreases as the number n of subintervals increases.

For a function $f(x)$ which is monotone increasing, these formulas may be illustrated by the areas of inscribed and circumscribed rectangles involved in the area interpretation of the integral (see Fig. 5–1).

An obvious increase in accuracy may be obtained by taking the average of $\underline{J}$ and $\bar{J}$ rather than either one individually, since this average

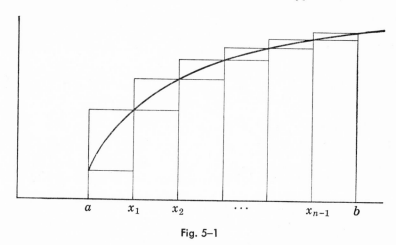

Fig. 5–1

and the integral both lie between these individual estimates.

$$\underline{J} \leq \frac{(\underline{J} + \bar{J})}{2} \leq \bar{J}.$$

The formula

$$\int_a^b f(x)\ dx \cong \frac{(\underline{J} + \bar{J})}{2}$$

is called the *trapezoidal rule* since it is equivalent to inscribing trapezoids in the area, rather than rectangles. This also may be thought of as the result of replacing the $f(x)$ by a series of first-degree functions representing the lines joining the points with ordinates $f(x_i)$ (see Fig. 5–2). In the case of a monotone function, the points x_i are the ends of subintervals Δx_i. When all Δx_i are equal, this rule may be written

$$(5\text{–}1) \quad \int_a^b f(x)\ dx \cong J_T = \frac{b-a}{2n}\,[f(x_0) + 2f(x_1) + \cdots$$
$$+ 2f(x_{n-1}) + f(x_n)].$$

Another simple rule may be formulated by using adjacent pairs of equal Δx_i, and evaluating $f(x)$ at the center of this double interval. Geometrically this can be considered as replacing the curve of $f(x)$ by a series of lines, for instance tangent lines, at these midpoints (Fig. 5–2). Here n must be an even number. This rule may be written

$$(5\text{–}2) \quad \int_a^b f(x)\, dx \cong J_N = \frac{b-a}{n}\,[2f(x_1) + 2f(x_3) + \cdots + 2f(x_{n-1})].$$

The trapezoidal rule, in the case of a positive function whose graph is concave downward, will underestimate the value of the integral, while

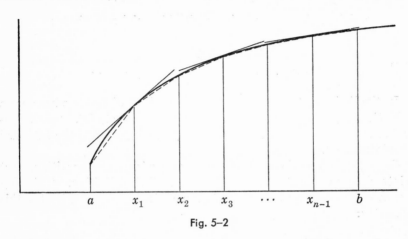

$a \qquad x_1 \qquad x_2 \qquad x_3 \qquad \cdots \qquad x_{n-1} \qquad b$

Fig. 5–2

the tangent rule will overestimate it (Fig. 5–2). An appropriate weighted mean of these two rules gives a much better estimate of the value of the integral. The rule derived from $J = \frac{2}{3}J_T + \frac{1}{3}J_N$ is identical with Simpson's rule:

$$(5\text{–}3) \quad \int_a^b f(x)\, dx \cong J_S$$
$$= \frac{b-a}{3n}\,[f(x_0) + 4f(x_1) + 2f(x_2) + 4f(x_3) + \cdots$$
$$+ 2f(x_{n-2}) + 4f(x_{n-1}) + f(x_n)].$$

Here n must be an even number as it is in the tangent rule. The geometrical interpretation of this particular mean value is that of replacing the curve of $f(x)$ by arcs of parabolas through three adjacent points of division. In order to study the errors involved in these and other rules, a more analytic form of derivation of their formulas will be given.

A polynomial $y(x)$ is used in place of the function $f(x)$, matching the value of the function at the $n + 1$ equally spaced points given by $x_0 = a, x_1 \ldots , x_n = b, f(x_k) = y(x_k), k = 0, \ldots , n$. Thus y will then be of the nth degree at most. It is easiest to represent y in terms of divided differences of the values $f(x_i)$. Starting with two points, we define

$$f[x_0, x_1] = \frac{f(x_1) - f(x_0)}{x_1 - x_0} = \frac{f(x_1) - f(x_0)}{\Delta x}$$

then

$$f[x_0, x_1, x_2] = \frac{f[x_1, x_2] - f[x_0, x_1]}{x_2 - x_0} = \frac{f(x_2) - 2f(x_1) + f(x_0)}{2! \, \Delta x^2}.$$

The general formula may be written with binomial coefficients:

$$(5\text{–}4) \qquad f[x_0, x_1, \ldots , x_n] = \frac{\displaystyle\sum_{k=1}^{n} (-1)^{n-k} C_k^n f(x_k)}{n! \, \Delta x^n}.$$

In the limit, as $\Delta x \to 0$, each of those divided differences becomes a derivative of $f(x)$ divided by the corresponding factorial. The coefficients are suggested by the expansion of $f(x)$ according to the extended law of the mean.

One of the properties of divided differences is symmetry with respect to interchange of any two points involved in their definition. This may be proved by reducing the symbol to the equivalent form which has this symmetry:

$$(5\text{–}5) \quad f[x_0, x_1, \ldots , x_n]$$
$$= \frac{f(x_0)}{(x_0 - x_1) \cdots (x_0 - x_n)} + \frac{f(x_1)}{(x_1 - x_0) \cdots (x_1 - x_n)} + \cdots$$
$$+ \frac{f(x_n)}{(x_n - x_0) \cdots (x_n - x_{n-1})}.$$

Interchange of any two of the arguments merely changes the order of the terms on the right-hand side. Because of this property we may write

$$f[x_0, \ldots , x_{n-1}, x] - f[x_0, \ldots , x_{n-1}, x_n]$$
$$= f[x_0, \ldots , x_{n-1}, x] - f[x_n, x_0, \ldots , x_{n-1}]$$
$$= (x - x_n)f[x_n, x_0, \ldots , x_{n-1}, x]$$
$$= (x - x_n)f[x_0, x_1, \ldots , x_n, x].$$

This emphasizes the non-repeated arguments x and x_n.

We may then form the successive identities:

$$f(x) = f(x_0) + (x - x_0)f[x_0, x],$$
$$f[x_0, x] = f[x_0, x_1] + (x - x_1)f[x_0, x_1, x],$$
$$\cdot$$
$$\cdot$$
$$\cdot$$
$$f[x_0, \ldots , x_{n-1}, x] = f[x_0, \ldots , x_{n-1}, x_n] + (x - x_n)f[x_0, \ldots , x_n, x].$$

Substitution from one equation into the next results in the general formula:

(5–6)
$$f(x) = f(x_0) + (x - x_0)f[x_0, x_1] + (x - x_0)(x - x_1)f[x_0, x_1, x_2] + \cdots$$
$$+ (x - x_0)(x - x_1) \cdots (x - x_{n-1})f[x_0, x_1, \ldots, x_n]$$
$$+ (x - x_0)(x - x_1) \cdots (x - x_n)f[x_0, \ldots, x_n, x].$$

We may interpret this as a polynomial approximation to $f(x)$ plus an error term of the form $f(x) = y(x) + E(x)$. This form is essentially equivalent to an interpolation formula of Newton. We may put this approximation polynomial in a more useful form by introducing the notation $x_k - x_{k-1} = h$, $x = x_0 + sh$; then s takes on integer values at the given points. If we denote $y(x_s) = y_s$, $E(x) = E_n(s)$, we have

(5–7) $f(x) = y_0 + s(y_1 - y_0) + s(s - 1)(y_2 - 2y_1 + y_0) + \cdots$
$$+ s(s - 1) \cdots (s - n + 1)(y_n - ny_{m-1} + \cdots$$
$$\pm ny_1 \mp y_0) + E_n(s).$$

If we use merely the first-order approximation and integrate over the given interval, we arrive at the form

(5–8) $$\int_{x_0}^{x_1} y(x)\, dx \cong h \int_0^1 [y_0 + s(y_1 - y_0)]\, ds$$
$$= h \left[y_0 + \frac{1}{2}(y_1 - y_0) \right] = \frac{h}{2}(y_0 + y_1).$$

This is the basis of the trapezoidal rule when summed over several successive intervals, so we use the subscript T for this formula. The error term for each interval,

$$E_T = \int_{x_0}^{x_1} (x - x_0)(x - x_1)f[x_0, x_1, x]\, dx,$$

may be simplified by evaluating the divided difference,

$$f[x_0, x_1, x],$$

in the form $f''(z)/2$, where z is some appropriate point of the interval (x_0, x_1). Then

(5–9) $$E_T = \int_{x_0}^{x_1} (x - x_0)(x - x_1)\, dx \frac{f''(z)}{2}$$
$$= h^3 \int_0^1 s(s - 1)\, ds \frac{f''(z)}{2} = -\frac{h^3 f''(z)}{12}.$$

This form of the error shows that when $f(x)$ is a first-degree polynomial, the use of $y(x)$ as a first-degree approximation results in a zero error, and the trapezoidal rule then gives the exact value. The geometrical interpretation of this fact is obvious.

When we use the second-order polynomial to approximate $f(x)$

integrated over the interval (x_0, x_2), we get a formula like Simpson's rule with a corresponding error term, indicated by the subscript s:

$$(5\text{--}10) \qquad \int_{x_0}^{x_2} y(x)\,dx \cong \frac{[f(x_0) + 4f(x_1) + f(x_2)]h}{3},$$

and since the integral $\int_0^2 s(s-1)(s-2)\,ds$ vanishes identically, we go to the next term to approximate the error:

$$(5\text{--}11) \qquad E_S = -\frac{h^5 f^{iv}(z)}{90}.$$

We find that this approximation gives exact values not only for any second-degree polynomial $f(x)$, but also any third-degree polynomial matching the same three values $f(x_0)$, $f(x_1)$, and $f(x_2)$. Let us define the term *degree of precision* N as the degree of the polynomial of highest order for which E is zero for all polynomials of equal or lower degree, with $E \neq 0$ for a polynomial of degree $N + 1$. Hence the precision of the trapezoidal rule is of degree $N = 1$ and Simpson's rule of degree $N = 3$. Many other important formulas may be obtained by using different polynomials $y(x)$ over different intervals.[M2][H2]

Example 5-1. Let us compare the use of the trapezoidal rule and Simpson's rule for the function $f(x) = \sin x$ on the interval $(0, \pi/2)$. If we use two intervals, applying the trapezoidal rule twice, we have

$$\int_0^{\pi/2} \sin x\,dx \cong J_T = \left(\sin 0 + 2\sin\frac{\pi}{4} + \sin\frac{\pi}{2}\right)\frac{\pi}{8} = (\sqrt{2} + 1)\frac{\pi}{8} = .948,$$

$$E_T = 2\left(\frac{\pi}{4}\right)\frac{3\sin z}{6} < .16 \text{ for each step;}$$

$$\int_0^{\pi/2} \sin x\,dx \cong J_S = \left(\sin 0 + 4\sin\frac{\pi}{4} + \sin\frac{\pi}{2}\right)\frac{\pi}{12} = (2\sqrt{2} + 1)\frac{\pi}{12} = 1.0020,$$

$$E_S = \left(\frac{\pi}{4}\right)^5 \frac{\sin z}{90} < .0033.$$

If we use 10 intervals, $h = \pi/20$, then

$$\int_0^{\pi/2} \sin x\,dx \cong J_T = \left[\sin 0 + 2\left(\sin\frac{\pi}{20} + \sin\frac{\pi}{10} + \sin\frac{3\pi}{20} + \cdots\right.\right.$$
$$\left.\left. + \sin\frac{9\pi}{20}\right) + \sin\frac{\pi}{2}\right]\frac{\pi}{40} = .9979,$$

$$E_T = 10\left(\frac{\pi}{20}\right)^3 \frac{\sin z}{6} < .0063 \text{ for each of 10 steps;}$$

$$\int_0^{\pi/2} \sin x\,dx \cong J_S = \left[\sin 0 + 4\left(\sin\frac{\pi}{20} + \sin\frac{3\pi}{20} + \sin\frac{5\pi}{20} + \sin\frac{7\pi}{20} + \sin\frac{9\pi}{20}\right)\right.$$
$$\left. + 2\left(\sin\frac{\pi}{10} + \sin\frac{2\pi}{10} + \sin\frac{3\pi}{10} + \sin\frac{4\pi}{10}\right) + \sin\frac{\pi}{2}\right]\frac{\pi}{60} = .999998,$$

$$E_S = 5\left(\frac{\pi}{20}\right)^5 \frac{\sin z}{90} < .000005 \text{ for each of 5 steps.}$$

5–3. HERMITE FORMULAS

Other formulas for numerical integration may involve values of the derivative of the function as well as values of the function. Many problems involve boundary values which determine the derivative at the end points of the interval, so an approximation formula involving these derivatives is not much more complicated than one involving values of the function only. The incorporation of the derivative values increases the degree of precision. One method of arriving at such formulas involves the use of equations obtained from the assumption of zero error in the application of the formula to polynomials of degree up to N. Formulas of this type are called Hermite quadrature formulas. We illustrate this method in deriving a formula involving values of the function and its derivative at both ends and the center of interval. For convenience and to conform to later derivations, we convert the interval (x_0, x_2) to a standard interval $(-1, 1)$ by the change of variable $x = sh$ with $x_0 = -h$ and $x_2 = h$. For a given function $f(x)$ we use the corresponding function $F(s) = f(sh)$.

We assume an approximate integration formula as follows:

(5–12)
$$\int_{x_0}^{x_2} f(x)\, dx = h \int_{-1}^{1} F(s)\, ds$$
$$\cong A_0 f(x_0) + A_1 f(x_1) + A_2 f(x_2) + B_0 f'(x_0) + B_1 f'(x_1) + B_2 f'(x_2).$$

When we apply this in succession to the functions

$$F(s) = (sh)^k \ (k = 0, 1, 2, 3, 4, 5)$$

we get a set of six equations involving the six coefficients A_i and B_i.

$$2h = A_0 + A_1 + A_2$$
$$0 = -A_0 h + 0 + A_2 h + B_0 + B_1 + B_2$$
$$\frac{2h^3}{3} = A_0 h^2 + 0 + A_2 h^2 - 2B_0 h + 0 + 2B_2 h$$
$$0 = -A_0 h^3 + 0 + A_2 h^3 + 3B_0 h^2 + 0 + 3B_2 h^2$$
$$\frac{2h^5}{5} = A_0 h^4 + 0 + A_2 h^4 - 4B_0 h^3 + 0 + 4B_2 h^3$$
$$0 = -A_0 h^5 + 0 + A_2 h^5 + 5B_0 h^4 + 0 + 5B_2 h^4.$$

If we consider the equations with left-hand sides zero we get

$$B_1 = 0, A_2 = A_0, B_2 = -B_0.$$

Then from the remaining equations we can determine the values

$$A_0 = A_2 = \frac{7h}{15}, B_0 = -B_2 = \frac{h^2}{15}, A_1 = \frac{16h}{15}.$$

The approximation formula then is

$$(5\text{-}13) \qquad \int_{x_0}^{x_2} f(x)\, dx \cong \frac{h}{15}\, [7f(x_0) + 16f(x_1) + 7f(x_2)]$$
$$+ \frac{h^2}{15}\, [f'(x_0) - f'(x_2)].$$

Example 5-2. Applying this formula to the example in Art. 5–2, we have

$$\int_0^{\pi/2} \sin x\, dx \cong \frac{\pi}{60} \left[7 \sin 0 + 16 \sin \frac{\pi}{4} + 7 \sin \frac{\pi}{2} \right] + \frac{\pi^2}{240} \left[\cos 0 - \cos \frac{\pi}{2} \right]$$
$$= \frac{\pi}{60}\, [8\,\sqrt{2} + 7] + \frac{\pi^2}{240} = 1.000026.$$

5-4. GAUSSIAN FORMULAS

A further improvement of the precision of quadrature formulas for a given number of points is obtained by allowing the location of the points to be determined by the matching equations. Let us consider a formula

$$(5\text{-}14) \qquad \int_{-1}^{1} f(s)\, ds = \sum_{j=1}^{m} w_j f(s_j) + E.$$

The m coefficients w_j and the m points s_j, may be thought of as $2m$ variables to be determined from as many equations. The maximum degree of precision is then $2m - 1$, since the $2m$ equations may be derived from polynomials s^k ($k = 0, 1, \ldots, 2m - 1$). Formulas of this type are called Gaussian quadrature formulas.

For example, with two points we have the four equations

$$2 = w_1 + w_2$$
$$0 = w_1 s_1 + w_2 s_2$$
$$\frac{2}{3} = w_1 s_1^2 + w_2 s_2^2$$
$$0 = w_1 s_1^3 + w_2 s_2^3.$$

The coefficients w_1 and w_2 in the equations with zero left sides can be eliminated to show that $s_1^2 = s_2^2$, and then we determine

$$s_2 = -s_1 = \frac{1}{\sqrt{3}}, w_1 = w_2 = 1.$$

Thus the formula

$$(5\text{-}15) \qquad \int_{-1}^{1} f(s)\, ds \cong f\left(\frac{-1}{\sqrt{3}}\right) + f\left(\frac{1}{\sqrt{3}}\right)$$

is exact for all polynomials of degree 3 or lower, and the error term in general involves the fourth derivative of the function. Other methods[H2] determine it to be

$$(5\text{-}16) \qquad E = \frac{1}{135} f^{\mathrm{iv}}(z).$$

If the two points are fixed by dividing the interval into three equal parts $s_2 = -s_1 = \frac{1}{3}$, the degree of precision is lowered to 1, in the formula

$$\int_{-1}^{1} f(s)\, ds \cong f\left(-\frac{1}{3}\right) + f\left(\frac{1}{3}\right).$$

Example 5-3. Let us compare these two quadrature formulas in the example $f(s) = \cos s$:

$$\int_{-1}^{1} \cos s\, ds = 2 \sin 1 = 1.68294$$

$$\cong \cos\left(-\frac{1}{\sqrt{3}}\right) + \cos\frac{1}{\sqrt{3}} = 1.68054$$

$$\cong \cos\left(-\frac{1}{3}\right) + \cos\frac{1}{3} = 1.88992.$$

Here the choice of the two most appropriate points has made the approximate value of the integral differ from the exact value by less than three units in the fourth significant figure. Similar formulas with more points are obtainable, with increasing difficulty involved in the solution of the matching equations.[H2] Other methods, involving orthogonal functions, show that the points involved in the Gaussian formulas of this type are related to the zeroes of the Legendre polynomials $P_m(x)$.[H2]

EXERCISES

5-1. Compare the results of using the trapezoidal rule and Simpson's rule to approximate the values of the following integrals to four decimals:

a. $\int_0^{\pi/2} \cos x\, dx.$

b. $\int_0^1 e^{-x^2}\, dx.$

c. $\int_0^1 \sin x^2\, dx.$

d. $\int_1^2 \frac{\sin x}{x}\, dx.$

5–2. Estimate the errors involved in the approximations in Exercise 5–1, using Eqs. (5–9) and (5–11). Compare these where possible with the difference between the actual values and the computed values. Use more than one value of h.

5–3. Use the approximation involved in Eq. (5–13) on the integrals in Exercise 5–1. Determine the values to five places.

5–4. Derive an approximate integration formula involving two points by the method of Art. 5–3. Apply this to the evaluation of the integral

$$\int_{-1}^{1} e^{-x^2/2} \, dx.$$

5–5. Apply the quadrature formula, Eq. (5–15), to the approximation of the following integrals to five places of decimals:

a. $\int_{-1}^{1} \cos 2x \, dx.$

b. $\int_{-1}^{1} (x^4 + 6x^2) \, dx.$

c. $\int_{-1}^{1} e^{\sin x} \, dx.$

d. $\int_{-1}^{1} x^2 e^{-x^2} \, dx.$

5–6. Calculate the approximate errors involved in use of the quadrature formula in Exercise 5–5 by means of Eq. (5–16).

5–7. Derive a Gaussian quadrature formula involving three points by the method of Art. 5–4. Apply this formula to the approximation of the integrals in Exercise 5–5.

6

Ordinary Differential Equations

6-1. SERIES METHODS

The technique of numerical integration will now be applied to the solution of the first-order differential equation,

$$(6\text{-}1) \qquad \frac{dy}{dx} = F(x, y).$$

This equation determines, at each point (x_0, y_0) of a given region in the (x, y)-plane, the slope of an integral curve of the equation through this point. Certain conditions on $F(x, y)$, which will be outlined later, ensure the existence and uniqueness of this curve. Under these conditions, we may start at the given point and by a series of steps follow along the integral curve as far as we wish, subject of course to computational errors in the various steps. This method contrasts with the analytical method of solution, which provides a functional relation satisfying the differential equation at all points of the region.

Integration of Eq. (6-1), with (x_0, y_0) as a starting point, gives rise to the integral equation,

$$(6\text{-}2) \qquad y = y_0 + \int_{x_0}^{x} F(t, y) \, dt$$

where t has been substituted for x as the dummy variable of integration.

This integral equation may be used to set up an iteration scheme by substituting an assumed form of y inside the integral to produce another form on the left side, as follows:

$$(6\text{-}3) \qquad y_{n+1} = y_0 + \int_{x_0}^{x} F[t, y_n(t)] \, dt.$$

This method is called the method of Picard.

In courses in differential equations the convergence of this procedure to a unique limiting function $y(x)$ may be shown to follow whenever $F(x, y)$ is a continuous function in a bounded region of the (x, y)-plane in which the additional condition

$$|F(x, y_2) - F(x, y_1)| < M|y_2 - y_1|$$

holds for all (x_1, y_1) and (x_1, y_2) in the region.[M1]   The latter condition is satisfied whenever $\partial F/\partial y$ is also continuous in the bounded region.

Example 6–1.   We illustrate this procedure by an example involving the differential equation $dy/dx = x^2 - y^2$, starting at the point $x_0 = 0$, $y_0 = 1$. The conditions for existence and uniqueness are here satisfied in any bounded region in the (x, y)-plane.   The slope at the point $(0, 1)$ is seen to be -1.   Hence we take as our first approximation to y the linear approximation $y_1 = 1 - x$. We get

$$y_2 = 1 + \int_0^x [t^2 - (1 - t)^2] \, dt = 1 - x + x^2,$$

$$y_3 = 1 + \int_0^x [t^2 - (1 - t + t^2)^2] \, dt = 1 - x + x^2 - \frac{2x^3}{3} + \frac{x^4}{2} - \frac{x^5}{5}.$$

It is obvious that the complexity of the procedure, evident in this simple example, limits its wide use for other than theoretical considerations.

Another method of only limited usefulness consists of repeated differentiation of the differential equation to determine the appropriate coefficient in a Taylor's series expansion of the solution about the point (x_0, y_0).

$$(6\text{–}4) \quad y(x) = y_0 + (x - x_0)y_0' + (x - x_0)^2 \frac{y_0''}{2!} + \cdots$$
$$+ (x - x_0)^k \frac{y_0^{(k)}}{k!} + \cdots.$$

Example 6–2.   In Example 6–1 we have

$$\begin{aligned}
y' &= x^2 - y^2, & y_0' &= -1, \\
y'' &= 2x - 2yy', & y_0'' &= 2, \\
y''' &= 2 - 2yy'' - 2(y')^2, & y_0''' &= -4, \\
y^{iv} &= -2yy''' - 6y'y'', & y_0^{iv} &= 20.
\end{aligned}$$

Then

$$y(x) = 1 - x + x^2 - \frac{2x^3}{3} + \frac{5x^4}{6} + \cdots.$$

This series is useful for extending the solution for small values of x, but since the interval of convergence is unknown, it is not often that such a series represents the solution closely for all values of x that are of interest.

6–2. EULER'S METHOD

The simplest method of step-by-step extension of an integral curve from any point, called Euler's method, involves a linear extrapolation along a line whose slope is given by the differential equation at the point. Here the size of any step must be small to approximate a curve which in cases of interest may deviate considerably from a line.

Example 6–3. Given

$$y' = x^2 - y^2, \ x_0 = 0, \ y_0 = 1,$$

let us extend this solution to $x = .5$ by steps of $h = .1$. The first step involves

$$y = 1 - x,$$

hence

$$y(.1) = .9.$$

Then

$$y'(.1, .9) = -.8,$$
$$y = .9 - .8(x - .1),$$
$$y(.2) = .82.$$

We proceed in the same way to get

$$y(.3) = .75676,$$
$$y(.4) = .70900,$$
$$y(.5) = .67463.$$

These values, approximating points of the solution, will be compared with others obtained by more accurate methods.

6–3. ADAMS'S METHOD

Improvement of Euler's method by using non-linear extensions in the form of polynomials of nth degree, covered by the general label of Adams's method, are obtained when data at a few points in the neighborhood of (x_0, y_0) are available for determining the approximating polynomial. The general technique of approximating a function when its values at a number of equally spaced points are known may be applied to representing $F(x, y)$ by a polynomial of the nth degree. This polynomial may then be integrated to find a corresponding formula for y. Thus we may write, by Eq. (5–7),

$$(6\text{--}5) \quad y(s) = y_0 + s(y_1 - y_0) + s(s - 1)(y_2 - 2y_1 + y_0) + \cdots$$
$$+ s(s - 1) \cdots (s - n + 1)(y_n - ny_{n-1} + \cdots$$
$$\pm ny_1 \mp y_0) + E_n(s).$$

If we write the corresponding expansion of $F(x, y)$ for $y'(x)$ in terms of the values of y_0', y_1', . . . , y_n', we have

$$(6\text{-}6) \quad y'(s) = y_0' + s(y_1' - y_0') + s(s - 1) \frac{y_2' - 2y_1' + y_0'}{2!} + \cdots$$

$$+ s(s - 1) \cdots$$

$$(s - n + 1) \frac{y_n' - ny_{n-1}' + \cdots \pm ny_1' \mp y_0'}{n!} + E_n,$$

$$(6\text{-}7) \quad E_n = s(s - 1) \cdots (s - n) \frac{h^{n+1} y^{(n+2)}(z_s)}{(n + 1)!}.$$

If we integrate both sides between limits k and s, using the fact that $dx = h\,ds$, we have

$$(6\text{-}8) \quad y(s) - y_k = hy_0'(s - k) + h(y_1' - y_0') \frac{s^2 - k^2}{2!}$$

$$+ h(y_2' - 2y_1' + y_0') \frac{s^3 - k^3 - \frac{3}{2}s^2 + \frac{3}{2}k^2}{3!}$$

$$+ \cdots + h \int_k^s E_n\,dt.$$

For different values of k, s, and n we have different functions $y(s)$, which furnish approximations to the points on the integral curve depending on known values of y' for $k = 0, 1, . . . , n$, as well as on (x_0, y_0). This transforms the differential-equation problem into one of solving a difference equation for values of the solution at certain points in terms of values of the derivatives at these or other points, in fact into a differential-difference equation. The general solution of such an equation is outside the scope of this book. We will merely use it as a tool in an iteration process which extends a solution from previously determined points to new points, taking care to control the errors in these steps so that progress takes place along a solution of the differential equation within some desired limits of approximation.

For $k = 0$, $s = 1$, and $n = 1$, we may make the simplest improvement on Euler's method in the form

$$(6\text{-}9) \qquad y_1 = y_0 + h\left[y_0' + \frac{1}{2}(y_1' - y_0')\right] + E_2$$

$$= y_0 + \frac{h}{2}(y_0' + y_1') + E_2,$$

where

$$(6\text{-}10) \qquad E_2 = \frac{h^3}{2!} \int_0^1 s(s - 1)y'''(z)\,ds = -\frac{h^3 y'''(z)}{12}.$$

We notice that this formula involves the value of y_1' at the unknown point. If we use an approximate value of y_1 to compute a first value of y_1' from $F(x_1, y_1)$, this formula may be used to recompute y_1. Such a formula which involves the derivative at the new point is said to be *closed*. Euler's method, which does not have this property, is called an *open* form.

Example 6–4. In the example $y' = x^2 - y^2$, we had

$$x_0 = 0, \ y_0 = 1, \ y_0' = -1,$$

and

$$x_1 = .1, \ y_1^{(1)} = .9, \ y_1' = -.8.$$

Then the new formula, Eq. (6–5), gives

$$y_1^{(2)} = 1 + .05(-1 - .8) = .91,$$
$$y_1' = -.8181.$$

A second application of the iteration procedure would produce a value

$$y_1^{(3)} = .909,$$
$$y_1' = -.8163.$$

The error term, Eq. (6–10), in this formula, which involves the third derivative, may be approximated by evaluating the third derivative at the origin from the differential equation, as in the Taylor's series method. We found previously that

$$y_0''' = -4,$$

so we approximate

$$E = -\frac{(.1)^3(-4)}{12} = .0003.$$

We may therefore expect our new value $y^{(3)}$ to be correct to 1 in the third decimal place. This type of iterative approach may be used with formulas of higher precision when more points have been determined.[M2][H2]

Extension of this procedure may be used to get values at $x = .2$ and $x = .3$ which are also correct to three decimals:

$$y_2 = .836, \ y_2' = -.6580, \ y_3 = .777, \ y_3' = -.5135.$$

6–4. MILNE'S METHOD

A convenient formula, developed by Milne,[M2] is used to predict the value of y_3 in terms of y_{-1}, y_0', y_1', and y_2'. It is of high precision since the error term involves multiples of the fifth derivative of y, even though the approximation of y' inside the integral is truncated at the second power of s.

We take $k = -1$, $s = 3$, and $n = 2$ in Eq. (6–8) and find

$$y_3 - y_{-1} = h \int_{-1}^{3} [y_0' + s(y_1' - y_0') + s(s - 1)(y_2' - 2y_1' + y_0')] \, ds,$$

from which

$$(6\text{--}11) \quad y_3 = y_{-1} + h\left[4y_0' + 4(y_1' - y_0') - \frac{8}{3}y_2' - 2y_1' + y_0'\right] + E_M$$

$$= y_{-1} + \frac{4h}{3}(2y_0' - y_1' + 2y_2') + E_M.$$

It is necessary to employ series or other methods to have data at enough points to use this formula. Since the formula does not involve the derivative at the new point, it is said to be open.

$$(6\text{--}12) \quad E_M = \frac{h^5}{4!}\int_{-1}^{3} s(s-1)(s-2)(s-3)y^v(z)\,ds = \frac{14}{45}h^5y^v(z).$$

This form of error follows from the fact that the corresponding formula with the third-degree term in s vanishes identically.

As a correction formula, we may use Simpson's rule,

$$(6\text{--}13) \qquad\qquad y_3 = y_1 + \frac{h}{3}(y_1' + 4y_2' + y_3') + E_S,$$

where

$$E_S = -\frac{1}{90}h^5y^v(z).$$

This may be derived from Eq. (6–8) by choosing

$$k = 0, s = 2, n = 2.$$

Then,

$$(6\text{--}14) \quad y_2 = y_0 + h\left[2y_0' + 2(y_1' - y_0') + \frac{1}{3}(y_2' - 2y_1' + y_0')\right]$$

$$= y_0 + \frac{h(y_0' + 4y_1' + y_2')}{3}.$$

Here the E_S for the third-degree term also vanishes identically, and so we have

$$(6\text{--}15) \quad E_S = \frac{h^5}{4!}\int_{0}^{2} s(s-1)(s-2)(s-3)y^v(z)\,ds = \frac{-h^5y^v(z)}{90}.$$

We may use the error terms in Milne's rule and Simpson's rule to estimate the truncation error in Simpson's rule, by assuming that the unknown arguments of the fifth derivatives are the same. If we subtract the values of y_4 obtained by the two methods, using superscripts for identification, and suppose that the calculated value of y_4' is sufficiently accurate, we get,

$$y_4^M - y_4^S = E_M - E_S = 29E_S.$$

Hence we can estimate E_8 by dividing the difference of the predicted and the corrected values of y by 29.

Example 6–5. Let us apply Milne's method to the previous example, $y' = x^2 - y^2$, using the starting values (Table 6–1) given by an earlier method.

TABLE 6–1

x	y	y'
0	1	-1
.1	.909	$-.8165$
.2	.836	$-.6580$
.3	.777	$-.5135$

Then,

$$y_4^M = y_0 + \frac{4h(2y_1' - y_2' + 2y_3')}{3}$$

$$= 1 + \frac{.4(-1.6330 + .6580 - 1.0270)}{3}$$

$$= .7331$$

$$y_4' = -.3774$$

$$y_4^S = y_2 + \frac{h(y_2' + 4y_3' + y_4')}{3}$$

$$= .836 + \frac{.1(-.6580 - 2.0540 - .3774)}{3}$$

$$= .733$$

$$y_4' = -.3773.$$

Here $y_4^M - y_4^S = .0001$, and hence E^S does not affect the calculation with the present degree of approximation. Similar steps give the values

$$y_5^M = .705, \ y_5^S = .7047,$$
$$y_6^M = .684, \ y_6^S = .6840.$$

Because the E^S values are so small, we may try to double the size of our steps by changing to $h = .2$. Using the values y_0, y_2', y_4', y_6' we can compute y_8^M to be .6922 with $y_8' = .1608$. The value of y_8^S then is .6898 with $y_8' = .1642$. When we use this revised value of y_8', we get $y_8^S = .6900$. The error is still less than 1 in the fourth place so we can continue with confidence using $h = .2$. Notice that the sign of the derivative changed from minus to plus between y_0 and y_8, indicating a minimum point of the solution. We have seen that the truncation error of each step has been negligible in computing the y of that step.

6–5. ERROR PROPAGATION

Let us consider the accumulated effects of various types of errors that occur in this method of numerical integration, applied to equations of the form $y' = F(x, y)$ in a bounded region of the (x, y)-plane.

The use of Simpson's rule will, at each step, lead to a numerical value of y_{n+1} subject to roundoff errors R_n in the computation, which we write

(6-16)

$$y_{n+1} = y_{n-1} + \frac{h}{3} [F(x_{n-1}, y_{n-1}) + 4F(x_n, y_n) + F(x_{n+1}, y_{n+1})] - R_n.$$

This y_{n+1} differs from the correct solution of the differential equation at x_{n+1}, which we denote by Y_{n+1}, by virtue of the truncation of the infinite series resulting in Simpson's rule. We indicate the error by T_n. Then we have

(6-17) $\quad Y_{n+1} = Y_{n-1} + \dfrac{h}{3} [F(x_{n-1}, Y_{n-1}) + 4F(x_n, Y_n)$

$$+ F(x_{n+1}, Y_{n+1})] + T_n.$$

The error at the $(n + 1)$th step then may be written $Y_{n+1} - y_{n+1} = \omega_{n+1}$ with known errors on the nth step given by $E_n = T_n + R_n$ due to trunction and roundoff. We then can write

(6-18) $\quad \omega_{n+1} = \omega_{n-1} + \dfrac{h}{3} [F(x_{n-1}, Y_{n-1}) - F(x_{n-1}, y_{n-1}) + 4F(x_n, Y_n)$

$$- 4F(x_n, y_n) + F(x_{n+1}, Y_{n+1}) - F(x_{n+1}, y_{n+1})] + E_n.$$

If we assume $F(x, y)$ has a continuous partial derivative with respect to y, ensuring the existence of a unique solution to the differential equation, and use the law of the mean, we may write, for some z_n between Y_n and y_n,

(6-19) $\quad F(x_n, Y_n) - F(x_n, y_n) = (Y_n - y_n) \dfrac{\partial F}{\partial y} (x_n, z_n) = \omega_n F_y(x_n, z_n).$

When this is substituted in the formula, Eq. (6-18), we have

(6-20) $\quad \omega_{n+1} = \omega_{n-1} + \dfrac{h}{3} [F_y(x_{n-1}, z_{n-1})\omega_{n-1} + 4F_y(x_n, z_n)\omega_n$

$$+ F_y(x_{n+1}, z_{n+1})\omega_{n+1}] + E_n$$

or

(6-21) $\quad \left[1 - \dfrac{h}{3} F_y(x_{n+1}, z_{n+1})\right] \omega_{n+1} = \left[1 + \dfrac{h}{3} F_y(x_{n-1}, z_{n-1})\right] \omega_{n-1}$

$$+ \dfrac{4h}{3} F_y(x_n, z_n)\omega_n + E_n.$$

Since $F_y(x, y)$ is uniformly bounded in the closed region, we may write $|F_y(x, y)| < K$. We also assume that the truncation and roundoff errors in any one step are bounded:

$$|E_n| \leq E \quad (n = r, r + 1, \ldots).$$

From the absolute values in Eq. (6–21) we can derive the inequality

$$(6\text{–}22) \quad \left| 1 - \frac{h}{3} F_y(x_{n+1}, z_{n+1}) \right| |\omega_{n+1}| < \left| 1 + \frac{h}{3} F_y(x_{n-1}, z_{n-1}) \right| |\omega_{n-1}|$$
$$+ \frac{4h}{3} |F_y(x_n, z_n)| \, |\omega_n| + E.$$

If we write this in the form of a difference equation for a variable e_n and with K in place of all the F_y's, we have

$$(6\text{–}23) \quad \left(1 - K\frac{h}{3} \right) e_{n+1} = \left(1 + K\frac{h}{3} \right) e_{n-1} + 4K\frac{h}{3} e_n + E.$$

The solution e_n of this equation will be shown to be greater than the value of ω_n for all values of n after those determined by the starting values. The starting values of e_n may be made arbitrarily small by independent determinations, so that $|\omega_n| \leq \bar{e} \leq e_n$ $(n = 0, 1)$. If

$$|\omega_{n-1}| \leq e_{n-1}, \quad |\omega_n| \leq e_n, \quad K\frac{h}{3} < 1,$$

then

$$\left| 1 - \frac{h}{3} F_y(x_{n+1}, z_{n+1}) \right| |\omega_{n+1}| \leq \left| 1 - K\frac{h}{3} \right| e_{n+1}.$$

and $|\omega_{n+1}| \leq e_{n+1}$. Thus, by induction $|\omega_n| \leq e_n$ for all n under consideration.

A particular solution of the difference equation (6–28) is the constant $e_n = -E/2Kh = -\lambda$. With $E = 0$ we may assume a solution of the difference equation in the form of a power of a constant $e_n = \beta^n$. On substitution in Eq. (6–23) we find that β then must satisfy the algebraic equation

$$(6\text{–}24) \quad \left(1 - \frac{Kh}{3} \right) \beta^2 - \frac{4Kh}{3}\beta - \left(1 + \frac{Kh}{3} \right) = 0,$$

or

$$(6\text{–}25) \quad \left(1 - \frac{Kh}{3} \right) \beta = \frac{2Kh}{3} \pm \sqrt{\frac{4(Kh)^2}{9} + 1 - \frac{K^2h^2}{9}}.$$

The two roots of this equation may be written

$$(6\text{–}26) \quad \beta_0 = \frac{2Kh/3 + \sqrt{1 + (Kh)^2/3}}{1 - Kh/3}$$
$$= 1 + Kh + \frac{(Kh)^2}{2} + \cdots$$

and

(6–27)
$$\beta_1 = \frac{2Kh/3 - \sqrt{1 + (Kh)^2/3}}{1 - Kh/3}$$
$$= -\left(1 - \frac{Kh}{3} + \frac{(Kh)^2}{18} + \cdots\right).$$

A general solution of the difference equation may be written

$$e_m = c_0\beta_0^n + c_1\beta_1^n - \lambda.$$

If we assume the error at $n = 0$ and at $n = 1$ may be represented by $\bar{e}$, we have the pair of equations to determine c_0 and c_1:

$$e_0 = \bar{e} = c_0 + c_1 - \lambda,$$
$$e_1 = \bar{e} = c_0\beta_0 + c_1\beta_1 - \lambda.$$

These give the values

$$c_0 = (\lambda + \bar{e})\frac{1 - \beta_1}{\beta_0 - \beta_1},$$
$$c_1 = (\lambda + \bar{e})\frac{\beta_0 - 1}{\beta_0 - \beta_1}.$$

These values make the appropriate solution

(6–28)
$$e_n = \frac{\lambda + \bar{e}}{\beta_0 - \beta_1}[(1 - \beta_1)\beta_0^n + (\beta_0 - 1)\beta_1^n] - \lambda.$$

This relates the maximum error upon the nth application of Simpson's rule to the basic constants $\bar{e}$, K, E, and h. If F_y may be represented by $\pm K$ in the region of interest, we see that either β_0 or β_1 is greater than 1. Hence one of the terms in e_n will grow with n, so we find that Simpson's rule is unstable because of the growth of this parasitic error. For a given set of values of the above constants, we can estimate the size of the error ω_n by calculating the corresponding value of e_n.

Example 6–6. In our example, with

$$y' = x^2 - y^2, \quad y(0) = 1,$$

we have $F_y = -2y$, and hence K is less than 2 for the region $0 \le x \le 1$. If we make $E = 10^{-5}$, $\bar{e} = 10^{-5}$, and $h = .1$, then we have $\lambda = -5 \times 10^{-5}$, $\beta_0 \cong 1 - .2$, and $\beta_1 \cong -(1 + .07)$, so that $\beta_0 - \beta_1 \cong 1.9$. The error bound e_n is approximated by

$$e_n = \frac{-4 \times 10^{-5}}{1.9}[-.07(.8)^n - .2(-1.07)^n]$$
$$= .15 \times 10^{-5}[(.8)^n + 3(-1.07)^n].$$

Hence, for values of n up to 10, we find the value of this bound is still of order 10^{-4}, but for $n = 20$ it becomes larger than 10^{-4}. We may improve β_1 by decreasing h, but for large enough n, the error bound will grow without limit. A general discussion of this effect is given in the references.[H1][H2]

6–6. RUNGE-KUTTA METHOD

The methods for numerical integration of differential equations given in the preceding articles are characterized by successive stepwise progression from an initial point through equal steps to a final desired location, using data depending upon several intervening points in each step.   The number of steps, and hence the size of a step, may be chosen subject to conditions of convergence and limitation of error.   Another method, due originally to Runge and extended by Kutta and others, uses values computed from points within the step in question, without reference to calculated values outside this interval.   These processes are self-starting and self-consistent, although propagation of errors from step to step results from the use of computed values at the end of one step for initial data in the next.   Another advantage is the independent choice of the size of the step, which may be increased to speed up the progression or decreased to lower truncation errors without recalculation of previous data.

The Runge method is based on an extension of the law of the mean by calculating more than one value of the derivative to replace the truncation error in the series.   For the differential system,

$$(6\text{–}29) \qquad y' = F(x, y), \quad y = y_0 \text{ at } x = x_0,$$

we use an approximate computation for y in the form

$$(6\text{–}30) \quad y_{n+1} = y_n + h[\alpha_0 F(x_n, y_n) + \alpha_1 F(x_n + m_1 h, y_n + t_1 k_0) + \cdots$$
$$+ \alpha_r F(x_n + m_r h, y_n + t_r k_0 + t'_r k_1 + \cdots + t_r^{(r-1)} k_{r-1}],$$

where the m's, t's, α's, and k's are constants to be determined.   In its simplest form we have

$$(6\text{–}31) \qquad y_{n+1} = y_n + \alpha_0 k_0 + \alpha_1 k_1$$

which we may compare with the law of the mean,

$$(6\text{–}32) \qquad y_{n+1} = y_n + (x_{n+1} - x_n) F[z, y(z)],$$

where z is an appropriate chosen point between x_{n+1} and x_n.   Since the values of k are to be calculated sequentially, we may write

$$k_0 = hF(x_n, y_n) = hF,$$
$$k_1 = hF(x_n + m_1 h, y_n + t_1 k_0).$$

We expand this latter expression about the point (x_n, y_n) as if x and y were independent, measuring F and its partial derivatives only at this point. Then, truncating to terms of order h^3, we have

$$(6\text{-}33) \quad k_1 = h\left[F + m_1hF_x + t_1k_0F_y + \frac{1}{2}m_1^2h^2F_{xx} + m_1t_1hk_0F_{xy} + \frac{1}{2}t_1^2k_0^2F_{yy} \right]$$

$$= hF + h^2(m_1F_x + t_1FF_y) + \frac{h^3}{2}(m_1^2F_{xx} + 2m_1t_1FF_{xy}$$
$$+ t_1^2F^2F_{yy}).$$

When substituted into Eq. (6–31), this gives

$$(6\text{-}34) \quad y_{n+1} = y_n + h(\alpha_0 + \alpha_1)F + h^2\alpha_1(m_1F_x + t_1FF_y)$$
$$+ \frac{h^3\alpha_1}{2}(m_1^2F_{xx} + 2m_1t_1FF_{xy} + t_1^2F^2F_{yy}).$$

The Maclaurin series expansion of y about (x_n, y_n) in powers of h, where $h = x_{n+1} - x_n$, truncated to terms of order h^3, gives

$$(6\text{-}35) \quad y_{n+1} = y_n + hF + \frac{h^2}{2}(F_x + FF_y)$$
$$+ \frac{h^3}{6}[F_{xx} + 2FF_{xy} + F^2F_{yy} + F_y(F_x + FF_y)].$$

Comparison of these two forms leads to equations involving the coefficients α_0 and α_1 and the constants m_1 and t_1 as follows:

$$\alpha_0 + \alpha_1 = 1, \quad m_1\alpha_1 = \frac{1}{2}, \quad t_1\alpha_1 = \frac{1}{2},$$
$$(6\text{-}36)$$
$$\frac{m_1^2\alpha_1}{2} = \frac{1}{6}, \quad \frac{m_1t_1\alpha_1}{2} = \frac{1}{6}, \quad \frac{t_1^2\alpha_1}{2} = \frac{1}{6}.$$

The solution of these six equations is possible because they are dependent. The second and the fourth give $m_1 = \frac{2}{3}$ and $\alpha_1 = \frac{3}{4}$; then the others are all satisfied when $\alpha_0 = \frac{1}{4}$ and $t_1 = \frac{2}{3}$. Thus,

$$(6\text{-}37) \quad y_{n+1} = y_n + \frac{h}{4}F(x_n, y_n) + 3F\left(x_n + \frac{2h}{3}, y_n + \frac{2}{3}k_0\right).$$

This two-term formula is of little significance since the new truncation error, including the terms resulting from the failure to satisfy all the matching conditions for third-order terms in Eq. (6–35), is therefore of third order in h. A corresponding formula with one more term,

$$(6\text{-}38) \quad y_{n+1} = y_n + \alpha_0k_0 + \alpha_1k_1 + \alpha_2k_2,$$

may be derived by expanding k_2 as follows:

$$(6\text{-}39) \quad k_2 = hF(x_n + m_2h, y_n + t_2k_0 + t_2'k_1)$$
$$= hF[x_n + m_2h, y_n + t_2k_0 + t_2'Fh + t_2'(m_1F_x + t_1FF_y)h^2]$$
$$= hF + h^2[m_2F_x + (t_2 + t_2')FF_y]$$
$$+ \frac{h^3}{2}[m_2^2F_{xx} + 2m_2(t_2 + t_2')FF_{xy} + (t_2 + t_2')^2F^2F_{yy}$$
$$+ 2t_2'(m_1F_x + t_1FF_y)].$$

Then we write the expansion of y_{n+1} to terms in h^3:

$$(6\text{–}40) \quad y_{n+1} = y_n + h(\alpha_0 + \alpha_1 + \alpha_2)F + h^2(\alpha_1 m_1 + \alpha_2 m_2)F_x$$
$$+ h^2[\alpha_1 t_1 + \alpha_2(t_2 + t_2')]FF_y + \frac{h^3}{2}(\alpha_1 m_1^2 + \alpha_2 m_2^2)F_{xx}$$
$$+ \frac{h^3}{2}[\alpha_1 m_1 t_1 + \alpha_2 m_2(t_2 + t_2')]FF_{xy} + \frac{h^3}{2}[\alpha_1 t_1^2 + \alpha_2(t_2 + t_2')^2]F^2 F_{yy}$$
$$+ h^3 \alpha_2 t_2' m_1 F_x F_y + h^3 \alpha_2 t_1 t_2' F F_y^2.$$

By comparing with the series in Eq. (6–35), we get the equations for the constants:

$$\alpha_0 + \alpha_1 + \alpha_2 = 1, \qquad \alpha_1 m_1 + \alpha_2 m_2 = \frac{1}{2},$$

$$\alpha_1 t_1 + \alpha_2 t_2 + \alpha_2 t_2' = \frac{1}{2},$$

$$(6\text{–}41) \quad \alpha_1 m_1^2 + \alpha_2 m_2^2 = \frac{1}{3}, \qquad \alpha_1 m_1 t_1 + \alpha_2 m_2 t_2 + \alpha_2 m_2 t_2' = \frac{1}{3},$$

$$\alpha_1 t_1^2 + \alpha_2(t_2 + t_2')^2 = \frac{1}{3}, \qquad \alpha_2 t_2' m_1 = \frac{1}{6}, \qquad \alpha_2 t_1 t_2' = \frac{1}{6}.$$

These eight equations are not independent, as we show by introducing the relations

$$t_1 = m_1,$$
$$t_2 + t_2' = m_2,$$

which reduce the eight equations to four:

$$(6\text{–}42) \quad \begin{array}{cc} \alpha_0 + \alpha_1 + \alpha_2 = 1, & \alpha_1 m_1 + \alpha_2 m_2 = \frac{1}{2}, \\[2mm] \alpha_1 m_1^2 + \alpha_2 m_2^2 = \frac{1}{3}, & \alpha_2 m_1 t_2' = \frac{1}{6}. \end{array}$$

Since there are six constants and only four equations, two arbitrary choices still can be made. Several formulas of this type have been derived by particular choices, such as $\alpha_0 = 0$, $\alpha_1 = 0$, $m_2 = 0$, or $m_2 = t_2'$.

From $\alpha_1 = 0$ we get $m_2 = \frac{2}{3}$, $\alpha_2 = \frac{3}{4}$, $\alpha_1 = \frac{1}{4}$ and $m_1 t_2' = \frac{2}{9}$. Further choice of $t_2' = m_2 = \frac{2}{3}$ gives $m_1 = \frac{1}{3}$, and we have Heun's formulas.

$$k_0 = hF$$

$$k_1 = hF\left(x_n + \frac{1}{3}h, \; y_n + \frac{1}{3}k_0\right)$$

$$(6\text{–}43) \quad k_2 = hF\left(x_n + \frac{2}{3}h, \; y_n + \frac{2}{3}k_1\right)$$

$$y_{n+1} = y_n + \frac{1}{4}(k_0 + 3k_2).$$

Another result with $\alpha_1 = 0$, when we choose $m_1 = m_2 = \frac{2}{3}$, gives $t_2' = \frac{1}{3}$, and we have the formulas

$$k_0 = hF$$

$$k_1 = hF\left(x_n + \frac{2}{3}h,\ y_n + \frac{2}{3}k_0\right)$$

(6-44)

$$k_2 = hF\left(x_n + \frac{2}{3}h,\ y_n + \frac{1}{3}k_0 + \frac{1}{3}k_1\right)$$

$$y_{n+1} = y_n + \frac{1}{4}(k_0 + 3k_2)$$

Other choices give Kutta's formulas

$$k_0 = hF$$

$$k_1 = hF\left(x_n + \frac{1}{2}h,\ y_n + \frac{1}{2}k_0\right)$$

(6-45)

$$k_2 = hF(x_n + h,\ y_n - k_0 + 2k_1)$$

$$y_{n+1} = y_n + \frac{1}{6}(k_0 + 4k_1 + k_2).$$

This reduces to Simpson's rule when $F(x, y)$ is independent of y.   A more symmetrical set of formulas is

$$k_0 = hF$$

$$k_1 = hF\left(x_n + \frac{2}{3}h,\ y_n + \frac{2}{3}k_0\right)$$

(6-46)

$$k_2 = hF\left(x_n + \frac{2}{3}h,\ y_n + \frac{2}{3}k_1\right)$$

$$y_{n+1} = y_n + \frac{1}{8}(2k_0 + 3k_1 + 3k_2).$$

Any one of these has an error term which is proportional to h^4.   A fourth-order system, due to Gill,[G] has special advantages for computer use, namely minimum storage requirements and low truncation error. It is expressed by the formulas,

$$k_0 = hF$$

$$k_1 = hF\left(x_0 + \frac{1}{2}h,\ y_0 + \frac{1}{2}k_0\right)$$

(6-47)

$$k_2 = hF\left[x_0 + \frac{1}{2}h,\ y_0 + \left(-\frac{1}{2} + \sqrt{\frac{1}{2}}\right)k_0 + \left(1 - \sqrt{\frac{1}{2}}\right)k_1\right]$$

$$k_3 = hF\left[x_0 + h,\ y_0 + \left(-\sqrt{\frac{1}{2}}\right)k_1 + \left(1 + \sqrt{\frac{1}{2}}\right)k_2\right]$$

$$y_{n+1} = y_n + \frac{1}{6}k_0 + \frac{1}{3}\left(1 - \sqrt{\frac{1}{2}}\right)k_1 + \frac{1}{3}\left(1 + \sqrt{\frac{1}{2}}\right)k_2 + \frac{1}{6}k_3.$$

Similar formulas of higher order can be derived by matching higher-order terms in the expansion. Precise calculation of the truncation errors does not follow from the methods used in the formulas of earlier articles, and they will be omitted from this book.

Example 6–7. As applied to the differential equation

$$y' = x^2 - y^2, \quad x = 0, \quad y = 1,$$

Heun's formulas with $h = .3$ give

$$k_0 = hF(0, 1) = -.3$$
$$k_1 = hF(.1, .9) = -.24$$
$$k_2 = hF(.2, .84) = .3(.04 - .7050) = -.1995$$

$$y(.3) = 1 + \frac{1}{4}(-.3 - .5985) = 1 - .225 = .775.$$

A second step gives

$$y(.6) = .682.$$

Example 6–8. The use of Gill's formulas in the system of Example 6–7 gives

$$k_0 = hF = -.3$$
$$k_1 = hF(.15, .85) = -.21$$
$$k_2 = hF(.15, 1 - .062 - .062) = hF(.15, .874) = -.22$$
$$k_3 = hF(.3, 1 + .147 - .379) = hF(.3, .768) = -.15$$
$$y(.3) = 1 - .050 - .021 - .127 - .025 = .777.$$

6–7. SECOND-ORDER LINEAR EQUATIONS

So far we have considered the numerical solution of only first-order differential equations, but similar methods can be developed for higher-order equations, too. One technique involves the introduction of new variables so as to separate an nth-order equation into a system of n coupled first-order equations. These equations are then subject to the same methods of approximation as have been developed in the preceding articles.

A special formula for a second-order equation may be developed when it can be written in the form

$$(6\text{–}48) \qquad\qquad y'' = F(x, y).$$

Equations involving the first derivative linearly can be reduced to this form by change of dependent variable. Given the equation

$$(6\text{–}49) \qquad\qquad y'' + P(x)y' = F(x, y),$$

the substitution $y = ve^{-\frac{1}{2}\int P(x)\,dx}$ produces the equation for v in the desired form:

$$(6\text{-}50) \qquad v'' = \left(\frac{P^2(x)}{4} - \frac{P'(x)}{2}\right)v + F(x, ve^{-\frac{1}{2}\int P\,dx}).$$

For the numerical solution of this type of equation we can develop formulas for representing the solution at a point in terms of values of the second derivative at nearby points, along with other values of the solution itself. These are derived in a manner analogous to those for first-order equations. These derivations are required in Exercises 6–9 and 6–10. An open formula may be used as a predictor, and then a closed formula used to correct the estimated value. The difference of these term values is then employed to estimate the size of the truncation error of the corrector formula.

A convenient set of formulas of this type is

$$(6\text{-}51) \qquad y_{n+1} = y_n + y_{n-2} - y_{n-3} + \frac{h^2}{4}\,(5y_n'' + 2y_{n-1}'' + 5y_{n-2}'') + E_1,$$

$$(6\text{-}52) \qquad E_1 = \frac{17h^6 y^{\text{vi}}(z_1)}{240},$$

$$(6\text{-}53) \qquad y_{n+1} = 2y_n - y_{n-1} + \frac{h^2}{12}\,(y_{n+1}'' + 10y_n'' + y_{n-1}'') + E_2$$

and

$$(6\text{-}54) \qquad E_2 = -\frac{h^6 y^{\text{vi}}(z_2)}{240}.$$

Then E_2 is approximated by one-eighteenth the difference between the corrector value and the predictor value.

Example 6–9. If we apply this to the example

$$y'' = xy, \qquad y(0) = 0, \qquad y'(0) = 1,$$

using starting values obtained by a series solution, we have Table 6–2.

TABLE 6–2

x_0	y_0	y_0''
.1	.10001	.01000
.2	.20013	.04003
.3	.30068	.09020

The predictor formula gives

$$y(.4) = .30068 + .10001 - 0 + .0025[5(.09020) + 2(.04003) + 5(.01000)]$$
$$= .40214.$$

From this value we get

$$y''(.4) = .16086.$$

Then the corrector formula gives

$$y(.4) = 2(.30068) - .20013 + .00083[.16086 + 10(.09020) + 0.4003]$$
$$= .40214.$$

The equality to five places of these values of $y(.4)$ makes the truncation error here negligible and suggest an increase in h as soon as enough data are available.

EXERCISES

6–1. Use the method of Picard to get an approximate solution to the following differential systems correct to terms in x^5.

a. $y' = x + y^2$, $y(0) = 1$.

b. $y' = x^2 - xy$, $y(0) = \dfrac{1}{2}$.

c. $y' = x + \dfrac{1}{y}$, $y(0) = 1$.

d. $y' = x + \sin y$, $y(0) = \dfrac{1}{2}$.

6–2. Use Taylor's series to approximate the solutions of the differential systems of Exercise 6–1 to terms in x^5.

6–3. Use Euler's method to approximate the solutions of the systems in Exercise 6–1 by steps of $h - .2$ at $x = 1$.

6–4. Use iteration of Eq. (6–9) to improve the values obtained in Exercise 6–3.

6–5. Use Milne's method, outlined in Art. 6–4, to approximate the solution of the following systems to $x = 2$:

a. $y' = x^2 + \dfrac{1}{y}$, $y(0) = -1$.

b. $y' = y^2 - x^2$, $y(0) = -1$.

c. $y' = xy - y^2$, $y(0) = 1$.

d. $y' = x + e^{-y}$, $y(0) = 0$.

e. $y' = xy + e^y$, $y(0) = -1$.

6–6. Investigate the maximum error involved in the approximations in Exercise 6–5 by using Eq. (6–28) with different values of h and E.

6–7. Use Runge-Kutta methods to extend the solutions of the approximations in Exercise 6–5 to $x = 5$, using an h appropriate to the particular problem.

6–8. Establish Eqs. (6–45) and (6–47) by appropriate choice of constant in Eqs. (6–41).

6–9. Derive Eq. (6–54) by the following steps: (1) Express $y''(x)$ by Newton's interpolation formula in terms of a step variable s as in Art. 5–7.   (2) Integrate twice with respect to s over one interval to express y_{n+1} in terms of y_n, y_n', and differences in y_n''.   (3) Write the corresponding formula for y_{n-1} by changing the sign of h.   (4) Add to eliminate terms in y'_n and reduce to the form of Eq. (6–54) by truncation.

6–10. Devise a similar set of steps for deriving Eq. (6–52).

6–11. Use the technique of Art. 6–6 to investigate the propagated-error bounds appropriate to Eq. (6–54).

6–12. Apply the techniques of Art. 6–7 to the following differential systems extending the solution to $x = 1$ by appropriate steps:

a. $y'' = xy + y$, $y(0) = 0$, $y'(0) = 1$.
b. $y'' = x^2 + y^2$, $y(0) = 1$, $y'(0) = 0$.
c. $y'' = x^2 y$, $y(0) = 0$, $y'(0) = 1$.
d. $y'' + 2xy' = x^2 y$, $y(0) = 0$, $y'(0) = 1$.

6–13. Use the methods derived in Exercise 6–11 to investigate the error bounds in Exercise 6–12.

7

Partial Differential Equations

7–1. GENERAL REMARKS

Physical systems represented by partial differential equations occur in many important applied problems, and they present more variety in formulation and more difficulty in solution than most ordinary differential equations. The restriction to equations linear in the unknown function still leaves a very large class of important applications in heat transfer, elasticity, fluid flow, electricity and magnetism, neutron diffusion, and many other fields. We will illustrate several methods of numerical attack on such problems, but a general study of these methods would form a complete course in itself.

Partial differential equations in two variables involve a domain of application in a two-dimensional plane, and boundary values may be assigned in various ways along curves in the plane to determine the solution elsewhere in the domain, depending on the type of equation involved. For second-order equations, a classification into three basic types is useful in sorting out different boundary-value problems. The basic types are called elliptic, parabolic, and hyperbolic by reference to certain relationships to conic sections, although mixtures of these types also occur. The elliptic type involves the general form $0 = \partial^2 U/\partial x^2 + \partial^2 U/\partial y^2 +$ possible other terms of lower order. With no additional terms, it is called Laplace's equation in two dimensions, and its solutions are called harmonic functions. Boundary-value problems usually involve specifying values of the function or of its partial derivatives of first order along the closed boundary of a region, and then certain classes of solutions are determined at all interior points of the region. Steady-state heat-transfer problems, and many electrostatic and electromagnetic problems are of this type. Additional terms in these equations may represent heat generated inside the region, or sources or sinks of electrical energy in the

79

region.   Parabolic type equations involve the basic form $0 = \partial^2 U / \partial x^2 -$ $(1/a)\partial U / \partial t +$ possible other terms, and usually represent space and time variation of the solution in a one-dimensional region.   Here the initial values may be specified throughout the domain of the solution, and also boundary values of the solution or of its first derivative may be specified at certain points.   Without the extra terms, and with the constant a positive, the equation is called the Fourier equation.   The hyperbolic type involves the form $0 = \partial^2 U / \partial x^2 - a^2 \, \partial^2 U / \partial t^2 +$ possible other terms.   This, in its simplest form, is the wave equation, with constant a representing the reciprocal of the wave velocity in the medium. Because of this finite velocity, the solution at a given point can be determined only by effects that can proceed to that point from a source in the available time.   This makes an entirely different class of problems from those of the other two forms.

In general, numerical methods of solution of all these boundary-value problems depend on the use of a grid of points in the domain.   At the nodes of this grid, approximations to the solution are determined with the expectation that, with an extrapolation to an infinitely fine mesh, the solution would converge to the solution of the partial differential equation. In a two-dimensional system various coordinate meshes may be used. We will restrict ourselves to rectangular meshes, in which the spacings in the two directions may be different and related in a convenient way.

The basic relation between differences and partial derivatives may be obtained by truncation of a two-dimensional Taylor's formula:

$$(7\text{-}1) \quad U(x_P + h, y_P) - U(x_P, y_P)$$
$$= h \frac{\partial U_P}{\partial x} + \frac{h^2}{2!} \frac{\partial^2 U_P}{\partial x^2} + \frac{h^3}{3!} \frac{\partial^3 U_P}{\partial x^3} + \frac{h^4}{4!} \frac{\partial^4 U_P}{\partial x^4} + \text{higher-order terms,}$$

where we use the subscript $_P$ to represent a quantity evaluated at the point about which the expansion takes place.   Similarly,

$$(7\text{-}2) \quad U(x_P - h, y_P) - U(x_P, y_P)$$
$$= -h \frac{\partial U_P}{\partial x} + \frac{h^2}{2!} \frac{\partial^2 U_P}{\partial x^2} - \frac{h^3}{3!} \frac{\partial^3 U_P}{\partial x^3} + \frac{h^4}{4!} \frac{\partial^4 U_P}{\partial x^4} + \text{higher-order terms.}$$

Addition and rearrangement gives

$$(7\text{-}3) \quad \frac{\partial^2 U_P}{\partial x^2} = \frac{U(x_P + h, y_P) - 2U_P + U(x_P - h, y_P)}{h^2}$$
$$- \frac{h^2}{12} \frac{\partial^2 U_P}{\partial x^4} + \text{higher-order terms.}$$

By proper choice of a value for the argument in the fourth derivative, we may represent the truncation error as proportional to h^2.

A similar form for the first derivative may be obtained by subtraction, to provide an approximate formula with truncation error proportional to h^2, in the form

$$(7\text{–}4) \qquad \frac{\partial U_P}{\partial x} = \frac{U(x_P + h, y_P) - U(x_P - h, y_P)}{2h} - \frac{h^2}{6} \frac{\partial^3 U_P}{\partial x^3}.$$

7–2. LAPLACE'S EQUATION

In the reduction of a boundary-value problem to a form suitable to numerical solution, we cover the domain by a rectangular coordinate grid, in this case choosing the spacing h the same for both variables. Then Laplace's equation $\partial^2 U/\partial x^2 + \partial^2 U/\partial y^2 = 0$ may be replaced by the difference equation,

$$(7\text{–}5) \quad U(x_P + h, y_P) + U(x_P - h, y_P) + U(x_P, y_P + h)$$
$$+ U(x_P, y_P - h) - 4U(x_P, y_P) = 0.$$

Let us use the subscripts L, R, A, and B for left, right, above, and below to simplify the notation. Then we have

$$(7\text{–}6) \qquad U_P - \frac{U_L + U_R + U_A + U_B}{4} = 0.$$

This may be indicated schematically by Fig. 7–1.

More complicated representations may be derived, involving two neighbors in each direction, with truncation errors proportional to higher powers of h, but we will not use these forms.[8]

When the domain is rectangular, boundary values of U may be assigned at corresponding grid points of the boundary. Then an equation may be written for the value of U_P at each interior point, depending on neighboring values. If the grid has n interior points in each direction, n^2 equations are available, and it is possible to show that these equations always have a unique solution. As n increases, this solution converges to the solution of the corresponding boundary-value problem when the set of boundary values satisfies certain conditions.

Example 7–1. Let us consider a problem involving the steady state of temperature in a rectangle 5 ft × 6 ft, one 5-ft edge of which is maintained at a temperature that is highest, say 100°, at its middle and falling linearly to zero at the corners, and the other edges are maintained at zero. Let us start with a grid with spacing $h = 1$ ft. Because of symmetry, some temperatures will match, so we may reduce the total number of unknowns in this case from twelve to eight. Let us refer to the individual nodes by numbered subscripts according to Fig. 7–2.

4×5

$$-\tfrac{1}{4}$$
$$\bigcirc$$
$$U_A$$

$$-\tfrac{1}{4} \qquad 1 \qquad -\tfrac{1}{4}$$
$$\bigcirc \qquad \bigcirc \qquad \bigcirc$$
$$U_L \qquad U_P \qquad U_R$$
$$-\tfrac{1}{4}$$
$$\bigcirc$$
$$U_B$$

Fig. 7–1

2	1	2
4	3	4
6	5	6
8	7	8

Fig. 7–2

The following eight equations then can be written, using the form in Fig. 7–1 as a pattern

$$U_1 - \frac{2U_2 + U_3 + 100}{4} = 0,$$

$$U_2 - \frac{U_1 + U_4 + 50}{4} = 0,$$

$$U_3 - \frac{U_1 + 2U_4 + U_5}{4} = 0,$$

$$U_4 - \frac{U_2 + U_3 + U_6}{4} = 0,$$

$$U_5 - \frac{U_3 + 2U_6 + U_7}{4} = 0,$$

$$U_6 - \frac{U_4 + U_5 + U_8}{4} = 0,$$

$$U_7 - \frac{U_5 + 2U_8}{4} = 0,$$

$$U_8 - \frac{U_6 + U_7}{4} = 0.$$

These equations may be solved by any of the methods of Chapter 2, but iteration procedures applied to an assumed initial set of values of U_k often are used, especially when the number of points involved makes the matrices difficult to handle.

In our example, an initial choice of $U_k^{(0)} = 0$ $(k = 1, \ldots, 8)$ gives an approximate solution, following the Gauss-Seidel method (sometimes called the Liebmann method when applied to partial differential equations problems). This solution is shown in Table 7–1.

The rate of convergence of this method is rather slow. A procedure for increasing this rate involves extrapolating in the direction of change somewhat more than the amount indicated by the approximation formula. This may be written in the form

(7–7) $$U^{(k+1)} = U^{(k)} + \alpha(U^{L} - U^{(k)}),$$

TABLE 7–1

Approximation	U_1	U_2	U_3	U_4	U_5	U_6	U_7	U_8
0	0	0	0	0	0	0	0	0
1	25	19	6	6	1.5	1.9	.4	.6
2	36	23	12.5	9.3	4.2	3.5	1.3	1.2
3	39.6	24.7	15.6	10.9	6.0	4.5	2.1	1.7
4	41.2	25.5	17.2	11.8	7.1	5.1	2.6	1.9
5	42.1	26.0	17.9	12.3	7.7	5.5	2.9	2.1

where U^L is the value calculated by the Liebmann method.   Values of α between 1 and 2 are useful.   The optimum choice of α for most rapid convergence follows from a detailed analysis of the coefficient matrix in the system,[Y] and results in the formulas for rectangles:

(7–8)
$$\alpha_{\text{opt}} = 1 + \frac{\lambda}{(1 + \sqrt{1 - \lambda})^2},$$
$$\lambda = \frac{1}{4}\left(\cos\frac{\pi}{a} + \cos\frac{\pi}{b}\right)^2$$

where a and b are the dimensions of the rectangle in units of h.

When the correction changes sign or becomes small, it is best to drop extrapolation, i.e., set $\alpha = 1$.

Example 7–2.   For our example, $a = 4$ and $b = 5$, so we have

$$\lambda = \frac{1}{4}(.707 + .808)^2 = .575.$$

$$\alpha_{\text{opt}} = 1 + \frac{.575}{(1 + .62)^2} = 1.22,$$

Let us use a value of $\alpha = \frac{6}{5}$ to see the effect on our example, as shown in Table 7–2.

TABLE 7–2

Approximation	U_1	U_2	U_3	U_4	U_5	U_6	U_7	U_8
0	0	0	0	0	0	0	0	0
1^L	25	20	7.5	8.2	2.3	3.2	.7	1.2
1	30	24	9	9.8	2.8	3.8	.8	1.4
2^L	39	25.2	15.8	11.6	6.4	5.1	2.5	2
2	40.8	25.4	17.2	12	7.1	5.4	2.8	2.1
3^L	42	26	18.3	12.6	8	5.9	3.1	2.3
3	42.2	26.7	18.5	12.7	8.1	6	3.2	2.3
4^L	43	26.4	19.1	12.8	8.6	5.9	3.3	2.3

The increased rate of convergence is apparent. This is important in large systems in terms of the computer time in a given problem. We illustrate the temperature distribution in Fig. 7–3.

26.4	43.0	26.4
12.8	19.1	12.8
5.9	8.6	5.9
2.3	3.3	2.3

Fig. 7–3

Another aspect of such an approximation technique is the unequal importance of the various points of the grid. From Fig. 7–3 we see that the major temperature changes occur in the upper part of the plate. It would seem to be necessary to interpolate more points to determine the distribution more accurately. Let us consider the upper left-hand corner, and change the mesh size to $\frac{1}{2}$ ft. Some new points can be approximated by using diagonal points in place of the previous L, R, A, and B points in the approximation formula, since the diagonals form a rectangular mesh, and the change in spacing does not affect the approximation. We start with Fig. 7–4.

0	25	50	75	100	75
	a	e	b	f	
	g	26.4	h	43.0	
	c	i	d	j	
		12.8		19.1	

Fig. 7–4

By diagonals we have

$$U_a = \frac{50 + 26.4}{4} = 19.1$$

$$U_b = \frac{50 + 100 + 26.4 + 43.0}{4} = 54.9$$

$$U_c = 9.8$$

$$U_d = 25.3.$$

Then returning to the other grid, we get

$$U_e = \frac{50 + 26.4 + 19.1 + 54.9}{4} = 37.6$$

$$U_f = \frac{100 + 43.0 + 54.9 + 54.9}{4} = 63.2$$

$$U_g = 13.8$$
$$U_h = 37.4$$
$$U_i = 18.1$$
$$U_j = 28.2.$$

Figure 7–5 shows these new values.

19.1	37.6	54.9	63.2
13.8	26.4	37.4	43.0
9.8	18.1	25.3	28.2

Fig. 7–5

Of course, iteration may be used with this finer grid, and extrapolation may be applied to speed the convergence.

7–3. OTHER ELLIPTIC TYPES

Several other important problems can be reduced to partial differential equations of the type

$$(7\text{–}9) \qquad \frac{\partial^2 U}{\partial x^2} + \frac{\partial^2 U}{\partial y^2} - B^2 U = K,$$

where B^2 is a constant, but K is a function of the coordinates. Appropriate boundary conditions are applied to U at the extremities of the domain. This is the form of the two-dimensional neutron diffusion equation, with K as a source term. In this case the appropriate boundary conditions are the vanishing of the neutron flux U on an extrapolated boundary of the reactor. If we change the partial derivatives to differences, the equation can be reduced to the form

$$(7\text{–}10) \qquad U_P - b(U_L + U_R + U_A + U_B) = f_P$$

where

$$b = \frac{1}{4 + B^2h^2}, \qquad f_P = \frac{-K_Ph^2}{4 + B^2h^2}.$$

Here the coefficients depend on the size of the grid spacing. We apply this to a square domain with n^2 interior points, and use the condition $U = 0$ at all points of the boundary. We then set up n^2 equations in the unknown fluxes at the nodes of the grid. Again, many methods are available for the solution of these equations. Let us consider a method of iteration which depends upon solving simultaneously for the fluxes in a line across the reactor, and then using these results in the set of equations for the next line. This reduces the problem to the solution of n sets of n equations, a procedure for large n that may keep the solution within the memory capacity of a computer, when the n^2 simultaneous equations might exceed that capacity.

Example 7-3. Let us apply this to a simple example with nine interior points, labeled as in Fig. 7-6.

1	2	3
4	5	6
7	8	9

Fig. 7-6

with $b = .2$ and f given by the matrix

$$f = \begin{pmatrix} 1 & 2 & 1 \\ 2 & 3 & 2 \\ 1 & 2 & 1 \end{pmatrix}.$$

We start our iteration with the initial set

$$U = \begin{pmatrix} 2 & 2 & 2 \\ 2 & 2 & 2 \\ 2 & 2 & 2 \end{pmatrix}.$$

The equations for the points in the first line are

$$U_1 - .2U_2 = (.2)2 + 1 = R_1$$
$$U_2 - .2U_1 - .2U_3 = (.2)2 + 2 = R_2$$
$$U_3 - .2U_2 = (.2)2 + 1 = R_3.$$

These may be put in triangular form by subtracting the third equation from the first, retaining the third, and by replacing the second equation by one formed by adding .2 times the first and 4.8 times the last to the second. The set becomes

$$U_1 - U_3 = R_1 - R_3 = 0$$
$$-.2U_2 + U_3 = R_3 = 1.4$$
$$4.6U_3 = R_2 + .2R_1 + 4.8R_3 = 9.4.$$

The solution then is

$$U_1 = 2.04, \ U_2 = 3.20, \ U_3 = 2.04.$$

The next line gives the equations

$$U_4 - .2U_5 = .408 + .4 + 2 = 2.808$$
$$U_5 - .2U_4 - .2U_6 = .640 + .4 + 3 = 4.040$$
$$U_6 - .2U_5 = .408 + .4 + 2 = 2.808,$$

and the fluxes are

$$U_4 = 3.94, \ U_5 = 6.10, \ U_6 = 3.94.$$

The third-line equations are

$$U_7 - .2U_8 = \ \ .788 + 1 = 1.788$$
$$U_8 - .2U_7 - .2U_9 = 1.220 + 2 = 3.220$$
$$U_9 - .2U_8 = \ \ .788 + 1 = 1.788.$$

These give the solution

$$U_7 = 2.64, \ U_8 = 4.26, \ U_9 = 2.64.$$

This approximation to the solution is shown in Fig. 7–7.

2.04	3.20	2.04
3.94	6.10	3.94
2.64	4.26	2.64

Fig. 7–7

We observe that, although the symmetry of Example 7–3 would suggest that the first and last line fluxes should be the same, our order of solution has led to different values. Iteration, of course, is necessary to get a better over-all agreement in the fluxes, but it is apparent that the last fluxes calculated will always benefit from corrected values of the fluxes previously computed. In problems where the source terms f, and perhaps the boundary conditions too, are not so symmetric, this order of operation affects the rate of convergence. A technique, first suggested by Peaceman and Rachford, of varying the direction of solution by writing equations for columns alternately with those of rows, decreases the effect of this ordering.

Example 7-4. In our example this gives, for a second approximation to the first-column fluxes, the equations,

$$U_1 - .2U_4 = .640 + 1 = 1.640$$
$$U_4 - .2U_1 - .2U_7 = 1.220 + 2 = 3.220$$
$$U_7 - .2U_4 = .852 + 1 = 1.852.$$

The solutions in this second approximation are

$$U_1 = 2.49, \ U_4 = 4.25, \ U_7 = 2.70.$$

For the next column, the equations are

$$U_2 - .2U_5 = .498 + .408 + 2 = 2.916$$
$$U_5 - .2U_2 - .2U_8 = .850 + .788 + 3 = 4.638$$
$$U_8 - .2U_5 = .540 + .528 + 2 = 3.068.$$

The solutions are

$$U_2 = 4.19, \ U_5 = 6.33, \ U_8 = 4.34.$$

The last column produces the equations,

$$U_3 - .2U_6 = .838 + 1 = 1.838$$
$$U_6 - .2U_3 - .2U_9 = 1.266 + 2 = 3.266$$
$$U_9 - .2U_6 = .868 + 1 = 1.868.$$

And these give the solutions

$$U_3 = 2.71, \ U_6 = 4.36, \ U_9 = 2.74.$$

Thus we have achieved a more symmetrical form of the solution as shown in Fig. 7-8. Further iterations in both directions will provide a convergent solution of the original problem, subject only to truncation errors of the formula.

2.49	4.19	2.71
4.25	6.33	4.36
2.70	4.34	2.74

Fig. 7-8

7-4. PARABOLIC TYPES

The Fourier equation in one space variable and one time variable is the general equation governing the diffusion of some substance, say heat energy or chemical concentration, in a one-dimensional system, a rod or thin tube, from an initial state subject usually to some boundary conditions at fixed end points:

$$(7\text{-}11) \qquad \frac{\partial^2 U}{\partial x^2} = \frac{1}{a}\frac{\partial U}{\partial t},$$
$$U(x, 0) = g(x), \; U(0, t) = f(t), \; U(L, t) = F(t).$$

When this system is converted to a difference equation on a space-time grid, in which the space nodes are h apart, and the time nodes p apart, we get the form, using the simplest approximation,

$$(7\text{-}12) \qquad \frac{U_L^i - 2U_P^i + U_R^i}{h^2} = \frac{1}{a}\frac{U_P^{i+1} - U_P^i}{p}$$

where the superscript indicates the time.

This can be solved for U_P^{i+1} in terms of the other U's to give

$$(7\text{-}13) \qquad U_P^{i+1} = U_P^i\left(1 - \frac{2ap}{h^2}\right) + \frac{ap}{h^2}(U_L^i + U_R^i). = U_P^i(1-2m) + m(U_L^i + U_R^i)$$

The relative size of the space step and time step is incorporated in the constant $m = ap/h^2$. The convergence of the solution of the difference equation to that of the differential equation, as h is decreased, depends on the size of this constant, and can be shown[R] to require $m \le \frac{1}{2}$. The special case $m = \frac{1}{2}$ gives the relatively simple form,

$$(7\text{-}14) \qquad U_P^{i+1} = \frac{U_L^i + U_R^i}{2},$$

usually ascribed to E. Schmidt. This merely says that the temperature at a point at any time node is merely the mean of the temperature to the right and left of this point at the preceding time node.

Although convenient, this can be replaced by other and better forms. For $m = \frac{1}{3}$ we get another simple form,

$$(7\text{-}15) \qquad U_P^{i+1} = \frac{U_L^i + U_P^i + U_R^i}{3}.$$

Another form may be obtained by reversing the roles of i and $i + 1$ in the original form. This gives an implicit type of relation which converges for any value of m:

$$(7\text{-}16) \qquad U_P^{i+1} - (U_L^{i+1} + U_R^{i+1})m = U_P^i(1 - 2m).$$

Another stable form may be written

$$(7\text{-}17) \quad U_P^{i+1}(1 + 2m) - m(U_L^{i+1} + U_R^{i+1}) = U_P^{i-1}(1 - 2m) + m(U_L^{i-1} + U_R^{i-1}),$$

and in case $m = \frac{1}{2}$, we get the form

$$(7\text{--}18) \qquad U_P^{i+1} = \frac{U_L^{i+1} + U_R^{i+1} + U_L^{i-1} + U_R^{i-1}}{4},$$

due to Crank and Nicholson, which looks very much like the form used in the elliptic case.

Any of these forms may be used in a given problem to determine the temperature at the next time node for each space node in terms of previously assigned or calculated values. There are as many equations as there are space nodes, and the values are calculated sequentially in time from the initial values.

Example 7–5. Let us consider an example with

$$
\begin{aligned}
L &= 40, \\
a &= 5, \\
p &= 2.5, \\
h &= 5, \\
f(t) &= 0, \\
F(t) &= 100, \\
g(x) &= \begin{cases} 5x, \ 0 \leq x \leq 20, \\ 5(40 - x), \ 20 \leq x \leq 40. \end{cases}
\end{aligned}
$$

Here $m = ap/h^2 = \frac{1}{2}$ and we may use the simple form

$$U_P^{i+1} = \frac{U_L^i + U_R^i}{2}$$

at each of the space nodes. The initial values at these points are

$$U_1^0 = 25, \ U_2^0 = 50, \ U_3^0 = 75, \ U_4^0 = 100, \ U_5^0 = 75, \ U_6^0 = 50 \text{ and } U_7^0 = 25,$$

and the boundary values are $U_0^i = 0$, and $U_8^i = 100$ for all i.

$$U_1^1 = \frac{0 + 50}{2} = 25,$$

$$U_2^1 = \frac{25 + 75}{2} = 50,$$

$$U_3^1 = \frac{50 + 100}{2} = 75,$$

$$U_4^1 = \frac{75 + 75}{2} = 75,$$

$$U_5^1 = \frac{100 + 50}{2} = 75,$$

$$U_6^1 = \frac{75 + 25}{2} = 50,$$

$$U_7^1 = \frac{50 + 100}{2} = 75.$$

The form at $t = 2.5$ is shown in Fig. 7–9.

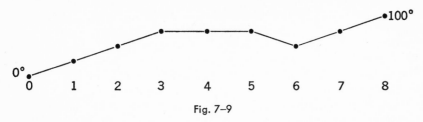

Fig. 7-9

A second application of the formulas gives, at $t = 5$, the pattern shown in Fig. 7-10. Repetition of this process many times leads to the steady-state form

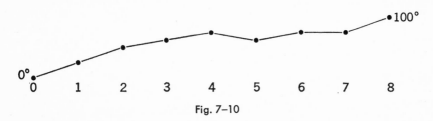

Fig. 7-10

given in Fig. 7-11. This illustrates the time involved in changing from the

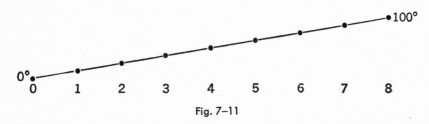

Fig. 7-11

initial to final state in this approximation. The solution of the differential equation requires infinite time to achieve this result, but in many cases the solution is very near the steady state in a relatively short time.

Example 7-6. Let us now use the Crank-Nicholson form on the same example, with time steps from $i - 1$ to $i + 1$, in effect doubling the time scale. We set up the seven equations at the unknown nodes at the time $t = 5$:

$$
\begin{aligned}
U_1 - .25U_2 &= .25(0 + 50) &&= 12.5 \\
U_2 - .25U_1 - .25U_3 &= .25(25 + 75) &&= 25 \\
U_3 - .25U_2 - .25U_4 &= .25(50 + 100) &&= 37.5 \\
U_4 - .25U_3 - .25U_5 &= .25(75 + 75) &&= 37.5 \\
U_5 - .25U_4 - .25U_6 &= .25(100 + 50) &&= 37.5 \\
U_6 - .25U_5 - .25U_7 &= .25(75 + 25) &&= 25 \\
U_7 - .25U_6 - 25 &= .25(50 + 100) &&= 37.5.
\end{aligned}
$$

These equations may be solved by any of the methods of Chapter 2. It is interesting to note that the matrix of coefficients has non-zero entries only along the main diagonal and the two adjacent diagonals. These tri-diagonal matrices occur frequently and have had special attention. An approximate set of values for $U(5)$ is $U_1 = 24.5$, $U_2 = 48$, $U_3 = 67.5$, $U_4 = 72$, $U_5 = 71$, $U_6 = 62.5$, $U_7 = 78$. These values could then be introduced in the Crank-Nicholson equations to get a new set of equations for the values of $U(10)$.

7–5. THE WAVE EQUATION

On applying difference methods to the solution of the wave equation,

$$(7\text{–}19) \qquad \frac{\partial^2 U}{\partial x^2} = \frac{1}{c^2} \frac{\partial^2 U}{\partial t^2},$$

we arrive at the difference equation

$$(7\text{–}20) \qquad \frac{(U_{k+1}^i - 2U_k^i + U_{k-1}^i)}{h^2} = \frac{U_k^{i+1} - 2U_k^i + U_k^{i-1}}{(cp)^2},$$

where subscripts refer to position and superscripts to time. We may solve for the new value of U at each point of the network in terms of earlier values at neighboring points, much as in the Fourier equation:

$$(7\text{–}21) \qquad U_k^{i+1} = 2(1 - m^2)U_k^i + m^2(U_{k+1}^i + U_{k-1}^i) - U_k^{i-1}$$

where m is the parameter relating the time and space grid lengths, $m = cp/h$.

In the case $m = 1$, we have

$$(7\text{–}22) \qquad U_k^{i+1} = U_{k+1}^i + U_{k-1}^i - U_k^{i-1}.$$

This may be interpreted geometrically in Fig. 7–12 as showing that the difference in values along one side of the diamond is equal to that along the opposite side. If we start at any point U_k^{i+1}, we may repeat this

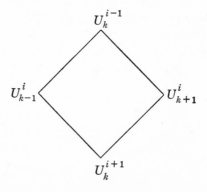

Fig. 7–12

relation i times, to write

$$U_k^{i+1} - U_{k-1}^i = U_{k+i}^1 - U_{k+i-1}^0.$$

Then we can also write

(7–23)
$$U_{k-1}^i - U_{k-2}^{i-1} = U_{k+i-2}^1 - U_{k+i-3}^0,$$
$$U_{k-2}^{i-1} - U_{k-3}^{i-2} = U_{k+i-4}^1 - U_{k+i-5}^0,$$

to get

(7–24)
$$U_{k-i+1}^2 - U_{k-i}^1 = U_{k-i+2}^1 - U_{k-i+1}^0.$$

When all these equations are added, the terms on the left cancel in pairs and we can write U_k^{i+1} in terms of U's with superscripts 1 and 0 and with subscripts between $k + i + 2$ and $k - i + 1$. This may be interpreted as an indication that only the initial values along the portion of the x-axis between the points indicated by these subscripts are needed to determine the value of U_k^{i+1}. Physically, this indicates that the finite velocity of the wave takes i units of time to travel a distance k, hence the choice of $m = 1$ means that $c = h/p$ is the velocity of the wave. The values along the entire initial line are effective only at certain points, and only after a long interval of time. The lines along which $x - ct = $ constant and $x + ct = $ constant, are called characteristic lines, or merely characteristics, of the differential equation. Then the two characteristics passing through a point (k, i), and extending back to the initial line, bound the set of points where the displacement U is involved in determining U_k^i, as indicated in Fig. 7–13.

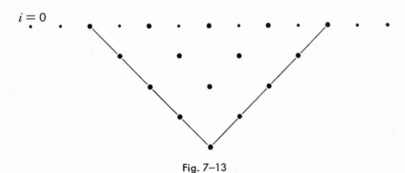

$i = 0$

Fig. 7–13

End-point conditions for a finite elastic string might involve fixed ends so that $U(0) = 0$, $U(L) = 0$. In case the equation refers to voltage waves on a high-frequency transmission line, the end-point conditions might be $U = 0$ for a shorted line, or $\partial U/\partial x = 0$ for an open line.

Example 7–7. Let us consider a line $10h$ units long with $U = 0$ at both ends. The initial values at $t = 0$ and $t = 1$ are required, representing the initial voltage and its time derivative. We make the derivative zero in our example, and indicate this as follows:

U^0	0	2	4	8	16	20	16	8	4	2	0,
U^1	0	2	4	8	16	20	16	8	4	2	0.

Then the next line can be filled in by using the difference equation for the various diamonds. It is immaterial which pairs of sides are used, since three points of the diamond represent known values, and the fourth the unknown. The third row of the example is

U^3	0	2	6	12	12	12	12	12	6	2	0.

This line and the second line now can be used to continue the determination of a fourth row

U^4	0	4	10	10	8	4	8	10	10	4	0.

Continuing, we get in succession

U^5	0	8	8	6	2	4	2	6	8	8	0,
U^6	0	4	4	0	2	0	2	0	4	4	0,
U^7	0	-4	-4	0	-2	0	-2	0	-4	-4	0,
U^8	0	-8	-8	-6	-2	-4	-2	-6	-8	-8	0,
U^9	0	-4	-10	-10	-8	-4	-8	-10	-10	-4	0,
U^{10}	0	-2	-6	-12	-12	-12	-12	-12	-6	-2	0,
U^{11}	0	-2	-4	-8	-16	-20	-16	-8	-4	-2	0.

Thus we see that the voltage distribution on the line has changed from positive to an identical negative distribution in 10 units of time, the time it takes a wave to travel the length of the line. During the next 10 intervals the process would be reversed, and the period of the oscillation then would be 20 units of time. Since $p = L/10c$, $20p$ is the period. In this case, the velocity c depends on the inductance and capacitance per unit length along the line.

Many other applications of difference methods to the wave equation are possible, but analytic solutions of problems of this type are so varied that the numerical methods have seldom been used.

EXERCISES

7–1. A square plate has one corner at a temperature of 100°. Along the adjacent edges the temperature decreases to zero at the next corners. The temperature of the other two edges is everywhere zero. Set up a network of nine interior points at which to determine the approximate temperature by the method of Art. 7–2, using symmetry to reduce the number of unknowns. Use the Gauss-Seidel method to determine these temperatures to one decimal place.

7-2. Increase the coverage of the hotter half of the plate in Exercise 7–1 by halving the spacing in the network, and determine the temperatures to one decimal place.

7-3. Use the extrapolated Liebmann method on the equations in Exercise 7–1 with $\alpha = \frac{4}{3}$. Compare the rate of convergence with that in Exercise 7–1.

7-4. Compare the convergence rate in Exercise 7–2 with the convergence rate in an extrapolated Liebmann method assuming $\alpha = \frac{3}{2}$.

7-5. A rectangular plate 5 ft by 4 ft has two opposite corners heated to 100°. Along the longer sides the temperature drops linearly to zero at the other corners. The temperature along the shorter edges is zero. Use the Gauss-Seidel method to approximate temperatures in a network of 1-ft mesh size to one decimal.

7-6. Apply the method of Exercise 7–3 to the problem of Exercise 7–5.

7-7. Apply the method of Exercise 7–9 to the problem of Exercise 7–5.

7-8. Use the method of Art. 7–4, to follow the temperature of a rod with $L = 50$, $a = 5$, $h = 5$, $p = 2.5$, $f(t) = 100$, $F(t) = 80$, $g(x) = 0$.

7-9. Use the method of Art. 7–4 to follow the temperature of a rod with $L = 90$, $a = 9$, $h = 9$, $p = 3$, $f(t) = 0$, $F(t) = 0$, $g(x) = 100x$.

7-10. Change Exercise 7–9 only by setting $f(t) = 90$, and follow the temperature change.

7-11. Use the Crank-Nicholson method to solve Exercise 7–8.

7-12. Use the Crank-Nicholson method to solve Exercise 7–9, making the necessary change in p.

7-13. Use the methods of Art. 7–5 to determine the voltage distribution along a transmission line $10h$ units long, if the voltage at $t = 0$ has the distribution $U(x) = x(10h - x)/h^2$, and if the voltage at the ends is maintained at 0.

8

Integral Equations

8–1. INTRODUCTION

Differential equations are equations which involve unknown functions in derivatives. One often encounters problems in which the unknown function appears in the integrand of a definite or indefinite integral. Analytic studies of these *integral equations* usually depend on series involving iterated integrals. We will consider numerical techniques for some of these problems, limiting our attention to the definite integral or Fredholm type of equation. One such equation takes the form

$$(8\text{–}1) \qquad f(x) = \int_a^b K(x, y)\varphi(y)\, dy$$

where $f(x)$ and $K(x, y)$ are given functions. The inversion of this integral, to give a result

$$(8\text{–}2) \qquad \varphi(x) = \int_a^b L(x, y)f(y)\, dy,$$

is relatively simple for a large class of functions K and f.

A more important class of equations takes the form,

$$(8\text{–}3) \qquad \varphi(x) = f(x) + \int_a^b K(x, y)\varphi(y)\, dy.$$

Here again it is possible in many cases to write

$$(8\text{–}4) \qquad \varphi(x) = \int_a^b L(x, y)f(y)\, dy + g(x).$$

Frequently the *kernel function*, $K(x, y)$, is continuous, but with a discontinuity in its derivative at the points $x = y$. Such cases often arise from the representation of a differential equation in integral form by means of a Green's function.

Example 8–1. A simple example of a Fredholm equation is the following:

$$\varphi(x) = x + \int_0^1 (x - y)\varphi(y)\, dy.$$

If we assume a linear functional form for the solution $\varphi(x) = Ax + B$, we have

$$Ax + B = x + \int_0^1 (x - y)(Ay + B)\, dy$$

$$= x + \left[Bxy + (Ax - B)\frac{y^2}{2} - A\frac{y^3}{3} \right]_0^1$$

$$= x + Bx + \frac{Ax - B}{2} - \frac{A}{3}.$$

This leads to the equations

$$A = 1 + B + \frac{A}{2}$$

$$B = -\frac{B}{2} - \frac{A}{3},$$

whose solution is $A = \frac{18}{13}$, $B = -\frac{4}{13}$. Hence the solution of the integral equation is

$$\varphi(x) = \frac{18x - 4}{13}.$$

Of course this equation does not require numerical approximation, but we will use this example to illustrate the method of approach to equations not so easily solved.

8–2. QUADRATURE METHODS

The definite integral in a Fredholm equation may be approximated by a quadrature formula involving the values of the integrand at certain points of the interval of integration. Since this closed formula requires the values of the unknown solution at these points, a set of unknown functional values is generated by each equation. We establish a sufficient number of equations to provide for the determination of these solution values.

If the quadrature formula involves values of the integrand at the points x_i $(i = 0, 1, \ldots, n)$, we replace the integral equation by the approximation,

$$(8\text{–}5) \qquad \varphi(x) = f(x) + \sum_{i=0}^n a_i K(x, x_i)\varphi(x_i).$$

We then evaluate this at each of the points x_i to get $n + 1$ equations in these $n + 1$ unknowns $\varphi(x_i)$, and solve the system of equations by one of the methods of Chapter 2.

Example 8-2. If we use Simpson's rule for the quadrature formula and choose three points on the interval $(0, 1)$, the integral equation

$$\varphi(x) = x + \int_0^1 (x - y)\varphi(y)\, dy$$

becomes

$$\varphi(x) = x + \frac{.5}{3}\,[(x - 0)\varphi(0) + 4(x - .5)\varphi(.5) + (x - 1)\varphi(1)].$$

Let us designate the unknowns as φ_0, φ_1, φ_2. The equations then reduce to

$$\varphi_0 = -\,\frac{2\varphi_1 + \varphi_2}{6}$$

$$\varphi_1 = .5 + \frac{\varphi_0 - \varphi_2}{12}$$

$$\varphi_2 = 1 + \frac{\varphi_0 + 2\varphi_1}{6}.$$

Iteration from an initial choice of zero for all φ's converges quickly, as in Table 8-1. The corresponding exact values are $\phi_2 = \frac{14}{13} = 1.07692$, $\phi_1 = \frac{5}{13} = .38462$, $\phi_0 = -\frac{4}{13} = -.30769$.

TABLE 8-1

Iteration	φ_2	φ_1	φ_0
1	1	.41667	−.30555
2	1.08796	.38387	−.30928
3	1.07641	.38453	−.30758
4	1.07691	.38463	−.30769

Since the truncation error for Simpson's rule is proportional to the fourth derivative of the integrand, in the previous example the approximate solution can be made exact by avoiding roundoff errors, and solving the equations in rational numbers. In other examples we may wish to use quadrature formulas with higher degrees of precision, for example Gaussian formulas. The inconvenience of evaluating terms at the irrational points may be lessened in equations involving even functions.

Example 8-3. Given the integral equation

$$\varphi(x) = x + \int_{-1}^{1} (x^2 - y^2)\varphi(y)\, dy,$$

let us use the three-point Gaussian formula, evaluating the integrand at $\pm\sqrt{\frac{3}{5}}$ and 0. The approximation becomes

$$\varphi(x) = x + \frac{5(x^2 - \frac{3}{5})\varphi(-\sqrt{\frac{3}{5}}) + 8x^2\varphi(0) + 5(x^2 - \frac{3}{5})\varphi(\sqrt{\frac{3}{5}})}{9}$$

Then the three equations, using φ_{-1}, φ_0, and φ_1 to designate the unknowns, become

$$\varphi_{-1} = -\sqrt{\frac{3}{5}} + \frac{24}{5}\frac{\varphi_0}{9}$$

$$\varphi_0 = \frac{-3\varphi_{-1} - 3\varphi_1}{9}$$

$$\varphi_1 = \sqrt{\frac{3}{5}} + \frac{24}{5}\frac{\varphi_0}{9}.$$

We see that

$$\varphi_1 - \varphi_{-1} = 2\sqrt{\frac{3}{5}}, \quad \varphi_0 = -\frac{1}{3}\frac{16\varphi_0}{15}.$$

Hence

$$\varphi_{-1} = -\sqrt{\frac{3}{5}}, \quad \varphi_0 = 0, \quad \varphi_1 = \sqrt{\frac{3}{5}}.$$

The determination of more points on the solution $\varphi(x)$ would require a larger set of simultaneous equations.

Again the exact solution is a polynomial, in fact $\varphi(x) = x$, and our values are precise, since the error in the Gauss formula is proportional to the sixth derivative of the integrand, which here is a third-degree polynomial.

Example 8-4. An example in which the exact solution is not a polynomial, and for which an approximate solution is appropriate, is

$$\varphi(x) = \sin \pi x + \int_{-1}^{1} \sin \pi(x - y)\, \varphi(y)\, dy.$$

Let us again use the Gaussian form of approximation, to arrive at the equation

$$\varphi(x) = \sin \pi x + \frac{5}{9}\left[\sin \pi\left(x + \sqrt{\frac{3}{5}}\right)\varphi\left(-\sqrt{\frac{3}{5}}\right)\right.$$
$$\left. + 8 \sin \pi x\, \varphi(0) + 5 \sin \pi\left(x - \sqrt{\frac{3}{5}}\right)\varphi\left(\sqrt{\frac{3}{5}}\right)\right].$$

Hence, with the abbreviation $\alpha = \sqrt{\frac{3}{5}}$, we have

$$\varphi_{-1} = -\sin \pi\alpha + \frac{-8(\sin \pi\alpha)\varphi_0 - 5(\sin 2\pi\alpha)\varphi_1}{9},$$

$$\varphi_0 = 0 + \frac{5 \sin \pi\alpha(\varphi_{-1} - \varphi_1)}{9},$$

$$\varphi_1 = \sin \pi\alpha + \frac{5(\sin 2\pi\alpha)\varphi_{-1} + 8(\sin \pi\alpha)\varphi_0}{9}.$$

These give the approximate values

$$\varphi_{-1} = -.190, \quad \varphi_0 = -.274, \quad \varphi_1 = 652.$$

Here obviously $\varphi(x)$ is a function whose general form is not indicated by these few values. The question of truncation error is complicated by the fact that different errors appear as constant terms in the equations, and they may affect the solutions of these equations, even when the individual errors seem negligible.

8–3. GREEN'S FUNCTIONS

One form of integral equation arises from the representation of a differential system in integral form. A differential equation of the form

$$(8\text{–}6) \qquad \frac{d^2y}{dx^2} = F(x, y) + h(x),$$

with boundary conditions $y(a) = 0$, $y(b) = 0$, may have solutions which are continuous, but whose derivatives are not continuous at some point of the interval (a, b). They may be represented in the form

$$(8\text{–}7) \qquad \varphi(x) = \int_a^b K(x, z)\{F[z, \varphi(z)] + h(z)\}\, dz,$$

where

$$(8\text{–}8) \qquad \begin{aligned} K(x, z) &= \frac{(x - b)(z - a)}{b - a}, \, a \leq z \leq x, \\ K(x, z) &= \frac{(x - a)(z - b)}{b - a}, \, x \leq z \leq b. \end{aligned}$$

The fact that $\varphi(x)$ thus defined satisfies the differential equation can be shown by writing it specifically and differentiating twice:

$$(8\text{–}9) \quad \varphi(x) = \int_a^x \frac{(x - b)(z - a)}{b - a} \{F[z, \varphi(z)] + h(z)\}\, dz$$
$$+ \int_x^b \frac{(x - a)(z - b)}{b - a} \{F[z, \varphi(z)] + h(z)\}\, dz;$$

then

$$(8\text{–}10) \quad \varphi'(x) = \int_a^x \frac{z - a}{b - a} \{F[z, \varphi(z)] + h(z)\}\, dz$$
$$+ \int_x^b \frac{z - b}{b - a} \{F[z, \varphi(z) + h(z)]\}\, dz$$
$$+ \left[\frac{(x - b)(x - a)}{b - a} - \frac{(x - a)(x - b)}{b - a} \right] \{F[x, \varphi(x)] + h(x)\},$$

in which the two terms in brackets add to zero; and

$$(8\text{–}11) \quad \varphi''(x) = \frac{x - a}{b - a} \{F[x, \varphi(x)] + h(x)\} - \frac{x - b}{b - a} \{F[x, \varphi(x)] + h(x)\}$$
$$= F[x, \varphi(x)] + h(x).$$

Also, it is easy to show that the boundary conditions are satisfied:

$$(8\text{–}12) \quad \varphi(a) = \int_a^a \frac{(a-b)(z-a)}{b-a} \{F[z, \varphi(z)] + h(z)\} \, dz$$

$$+ \int_a^b \frac{(a-a)(z-a)}{b-a} \{F[z, \varphi(z)] + h(z)\} \, dz = 0,$$

and similarly $\varphi(b) = 0$.

Hence it is possible to find a solution of a differential system of this type by applying numerical methods to the corresponding integral equation.

Example 8-5. Let us apply this method to the solution of the differential system,

$$y'' = xy + x, \quad y(-1) = y(1) = 0.$$

The corresponding integral equation from Eq. (8–7) becomes

$$\varphi(x) = \int_{-1}^1 K(x, z)(z\varphi(z) + z) \, dz.$$

We use the Gauss three-point formula, identify the values at the points $x = 0$, $-\sqrt{\frac{3}{5}}$, $\sqrt{\frac{3}{5}}$ by φ_0, φ_{-1}, and φ_1, and write $\sqrt{\frac{3}{5}}$ as α. The approximation then becomes

$$\varphi(x) = \frac{1}{9}[-5K(x, -\alpha)(\alpha\varphi_{-1} + \alpha) + 5K(x, \alpha)(\alpha\varphi_1 + \alpha)].$$

The unknown φ values satisfy the equations.

The three equations for φ may be written

$$\varphi_{-1} = \frac{5}{9}[-\alpha K(-\alpha, -\alpha)(\varphi_{-1} + 1) + \alpha K(-\alpha, \alpha)(\varphi_1 + 1)],$$

$$\varphi_0 = \frac{5}{9}[-\alpha K(0, -\alpha)(\varphi_{-1} + 1) + \alpha K(0, \alpha)(\varphi_1 + 1)],$$

$$\varphi_1 = \frac{5}{9}[-\alpha K(\alpha, -\alpha)(\varphi_{-1} + 1) + \alpha K(\alpha, \alpha)(\varphi_1 + 1)].$$

From Eq. (8–8) we find the values of the K factors with

$$K(x, z) = \frac{(x-1)(z+1)}{2}, \quad -1 \le z \le x$$

$$K(x, z) = \frac{(x+1)(z-1)}{2}, \quad x \le z \le 1.$$

Then at the points in question we have

$$K(\alpha, \alpha) = K(-\alpha, -\alpha) = \frac{1}{2}(\alpha^2 - 1) = -\frac{1}{5},$$

$$K(\alpha, -\alpha) = K(-\alpha, \alpha) \quad = -\frac{1}{2}(\alpha - 1)^2 = -\left(\frac{4}{5} - \sqrt{\frac{3}{5}}\right),$$

$$K(0, \alpha) = K(0, -\alpha) \quad = -\frac{1}{2}(\alpha - 1) = -\frac{1}{2}\left(1 - \sqrt{\frac{3}{5}}\right).$$

We may write the equations for φ_{-1} and φ_1 in terms of these coefficients:

$$\varphi_{-1} = \frac{5}{9}\alpha\left[\frac{\varphi_{-1}+1}{5} - \left(\frac{4}{5} - \alpha\right)(\varphi_1 + 1)\right],$$

$$\varphi_1 = \frac{5}{9}\alpha\left[\left(\frac{4}{5} - \alpha\right)(\varphi_{-1}+1) - \frac{\varphi_1 + 1}{5}\right],$$

or, making use of the fact that $5\alpha^2 = 3$,

$$(9 - \alpha)\varphi_{-1} + (4\alpha - 3)\varphi_1 = -3(\alpha - 1),$$
$$-(4\alpha - 3)\varphi_1 + (9 + \alpha)\varphi_1 = 3(\alpha - 1).$$

The solutions are

$$\varphi_{-1} = -\frac{3(\alpha - 1)[9 + \alpha + 4\alpha - 3]}{9 - \alpha^2 + (4\alpha - 3)^2}$$

$$= \frac{3 - \alpha}{9 - 8\alpha} = .7939,$$

$$\varphi_1 = \frac{3(\alpha - 1)[9 - \alpha - (4\alpha - 3)]}{3(9 - 8\alpha)}$$

$$= \frac{3(\alpha - \frac{7}{5})}{9 - 8\alpha} = -.6693,$$

$$\varphi_0 = \frac{5}{9}\frac{\alpha(\alpha - 1)}{2}(\varphi_{-1} + \varphi_1)$$

$$= -\frac{3 - 5\alpha}{18}\frac{2\alpha - \frac{6}{5}}{9 - 8\alpha}$$

$$= -.00813.$$

Although the examples have been limited to approximating only a few points on the solution, the use of more extensive forms of quadrature formulas would lead to similar systems of algebraic equations, whose solution by methods of Chapter 2 is then possible.

EXERCISES

8-1. Use Simpson's rule to approximate the solution of the integral equation

$$\varphi(x) = 3x + 2\int_0^3 (x - z)\varphi(z)\,dz.$$

Compare with the exact polynomial solution.

8-2. Use Simpson's rule to approximate the solution of the integral equation

$$\varphi(x) = x^2 + \int_{-1}^1 (x - z)\varphi(z)\,dz.$$

Compare with the exact polynomial solution.

8-3. Use the Gauss three-point rule on the equation of Exercise 8-2, and check with the polynomial solution.

8–4. Use the Gauss three-point rule to approximate the solution of the integral equation

$$\varphi(x) = 2x^2 + \int_{-1}^{1} (x^2 - z^2)\varphi(z) \, dz.$$

Show that these values check the polynomial solution.

8–5. Use Simpson's rule to approximate the solution of the integral equation in Exercise 8–4. Compare the values obtained with those of the polynomial solution.

8–6. Find the integral equation equivalent to the differential system

$$y'' + 4y = x, \quad y(0) = y(1) = 0.$$

Use Simpson's rule to approximate the solution. Check with the exact solution of the system.

8–7. Find the integral equation equivalent to the differential system

$$y'' = x^2 y + 2x, \quad y(-1) = y(1) = 0.$$

Approximate the solution by using the Gauss three-point rule.

References

C   CHIAO, B. T., LI, H. L., and SCOTT, E. J. "On the Solution of Ill-conditioned, Simultaneous, Linear, Algebraic Equations by Machine Computation." *Engineering Experiment Station Bulletin No. 459.* Urbana, Ill.: University of Illinois, 1961.

F_1 FADEEVA, V. N. *Computational Methods of Linear Algebra.* New York: Dover Publications, 1959.

F_2 FORSYTHE, G. E. "Note on Rounding-Off," *SIAM Review,* Vol. 1, No. 1, (1953), p. 66.

G   GANTMACHER, E. R. *The Theory of Matrices.* New York: Chelsea Publishing Co., 1959.

H_1 HAMMING, R. W. *Numerical Methods for Scientists and Engineers.* New York: McGraw-Hill Book Co., Inc., 1962.

H_2 HILDEBRAND, F. B. *Introduction to Numerical Analysis.* New York: McGraw-Hill Book Co., Inc., 1956.

M_1 MARTIN, W. T., and REISSNER, E. *Elementary Differential Equations.* 2nd ed. Reading, Mass.: Addison-Wesley Publishing Co., Inc., 1961.

M_2 MILNE, W. E. *Numerical Solution of Differential Equations.* New York: John Wiley & Sons, Inc., 1953.

O   ORDEN, A. "Matrix Inversion and Related Topics." Chapter of Reference R, p. 47.

R   RALSTON, A., and WILF, H. S. *Mathematical Methods for Digital Computers.* New York: John Wiley & Sons, Inc., 1960.

S   SOUTHWELL, R. V., *Relaxation Methods in Engineering Science.* New York: Oxford University Press, 1951.

T   TAUSSKY, OLGA (editor). "Contributions to the Solution of Systems of Linear Equations and the Determination of Eigenvalues." *National Bureau of Standards Applied Mathematics Series,* Vol. 39. Washington: U. S. Government Printing Office, 1954.

Y   YOUNG, D., "Iterative Methods for Solving Partial Difference Equations of Elliptic Type," *Trans. Amer. Math. Soc.,* Vol. 76 (1956), p. 92.

Table of Squares

of

Integers

1000–9999

n	0	1	2	3	4
100	1000000	1002001	1004004	1006009	1008016
101	1020100	1022121	1024144	1026169	1028196
102	1040400	1042441	1044484	1046529	1048576
103	1060900	1062961	1065024	1067089	1069156
104	1081600	1083681	1085764	1087849	1089936
105	1102500	1104601	1106704	1108809	1110916
106	1123600	1125721	1127844	1129969	1132096
107	1144900	1147041	1149184	1151329	1153476
108	1166400	1168561	1170724	1172889	1175056
109	1188100	1190281	1192464	1194649	1196836
110	1210000	1212201	1214404	1216609	1218816
111	1232100	1234321	1236544	1238769	1240996
112	1254400	1256641	1258884	1261129	1263376
113	1276900	1279161	1281424	1283689	1285956
114	1299600	1301881	1304164	1306449	1308736
115	1322500	1324801	1327104	1329409	1331716
116	1345600	1347921	1350244	1352569	1354896
117	1368900	1371241	1373584	1375929	1378276
118	1392400	1394761	1397124	1399489	1401856
119	1416100	1418481	1420864	1423249	1425636
120	1440000	1442401	1444804	1447209	1449616
121	1464100	1466521	1468944	1471369	1473796
122	1488400	1490841	1493284	1495729	1498176
123	1512900	1515361	1517824	1520289	1522756
124	1537600	1540081	1542564	1545049	1547536
125	1562500	1565001	1567504	1570009	1572516
126	1587600	1590121	1592644	1595169	1597696
127	1612900	1615441	1617984	1620529	1623076
128	1638400	1640961	1643524	1646089	1648656
129	1664100	1666681	1669264	1671849	1674436
130	1690000	1692601	1695204	1697809	1700416
131	1716100	1718721	1721344	1723969	1726596
132	1742400	1745041	1747684	1750329	1752976
133	1768900	1771561	1774224	1776889	1779556
134	1795600	1798281	1800964	1803649	1806336
135	1822500	1825201	1827904	1830609	1833316
136	1849600	1852321	1855044	1857769	1860496
137	1876900	1879641	1882384	1885129	1887876
138	1904400	1907161	1909924	1912689	1915456
139	1932100	1934881	1937664	1940449	1943236
140	1960000	1962801	1965604	1968409	1971216
141	1988100	1990921	1993744	1996569	1999396
142	2016400	2019241	2022084	2024929	2027776
143	2044900	2047761	2050624	2053489	2056356
144	2073600	2076481	2079364	2082249	2085136
145	2102500	2105401	2108304	2111209	2114116
146	2131600	2134521	2137444	2140369	2143296
147	2160900	2163841	2166784	2169729	2172676
148	2190400	2193361	2196324	2199289	2202256
149	2220100	2223081	2226064	2229049	2232036

5	6	7	8	9	n
1010025	1012036	1014049	1016064	1018081	100
1030225	1032256	1034289	1036324	1038361	101
1050625	1052676	1054729	1056784	1058841	102
1071225	1073296	1075369	1077444	1079521	103
1092025	1094116	1096209	1098304	1100401	104
1113025	1115136	1117249	1119364	1121481	105
1134225	1136356	1138489	1140624	1142761	106
1155625	1157776	1159929	1162084	1164241	107
1177225	1179396	1181569	1183744	1185921	108
1199025	1201216	1203409	1205604	1207801	109
1221025	1223236	1225449	1227664	1229881	110
1243225	1245456	1247689	1249924	1252161	111
1265625	1267876	1270129	1272384	1274641	112
1288225	1290496	1292769	1295044	1297321	113
1311025	1313316	1315609	1317904	1320201	114
1334025	1336336	1338649	1340964	1343281	115
1357225	1359556	1361889	1364224	1366561	116
1380625	1382976	1385329	1387684	1390041	117
1404225	1406596	1408969	1411344	1413721	118
1428025	1430416	1432809	1435204	1437601	119
1452025	1454436	1456849	1459264	1461681	120
1476225	1478656	1481089	1483524	1485961	121
1500625	1503076	1505529	1507984	1510441	122
1525225	1527696	1530169	1532644	1535121	123
1550025	1552516	1555009	1557504	1560001	124
1575025	1577536	1580049	1582564	1585081	125
1600225	1602756	1605289	1607824	1610361	126
1625625	1628176	1630729	1633284	1635841	127
1651225	1653796	1656369	1658944	1661521	128
1677025	1679616	1682209	1684804	1687401	129
1703025	1705636	1708249	1710864	1713481	130
1729225	1731856	1734489	1737124	1739761	131
1755625	1758276	1760929	1763584	1766241	132
1782225	1784896	1787569	1790244	1792921	133
1809025	1811716	1814409	1817104	1819801	134
1836025	1838736	1841449	1844164	1846881	135
1863225	1865956	1868689	1871424	1874161	136
1890625	1893376	1896129	1898884	1901641	137
1918225	1920996	1923769	1926544	1929321	138
1946025	1948816	1951609	1954404	1957201	139
1974025	1976836	1979649	1982464	1985281	140
2002225	2005056	2007889	2010724	2013561	141
2030625	2033476	2036329	2039184	2042041	142
2059225	2062096	2064969	2067844	2070721	143
2088025	2090916	2093809	2096704	2099601	144
2117025	2119936	2122849	2125764	2128681	145
2146225	2149156	2152089	2155024	2157961	146
2175625	2178576	2181529	2184484	2187441	147
2205225	2208196	2211169	2214144	2217121	148
2235025	2238016	2241009	2244004	2247001	149

n	0	1	2	3	4
150	2250000	2253001	2256004	2259009	2262016
151	2280100	2283121	2286144	2289169	2292196
152	2310400	2313441	2316484	2319529	2322576
153	2340900	2343961	2347024	2350089	2353156
154	2371600	2374681	2377764	2380849	2383936
155	2402500	2405601	2408704	2411809	2414916
156	2433600	2436721	2439844	2442969	2446096
157	2464900	2468041	2471184	2474329	2477476
158	2496400	2499561	2502724	2505889	2509056
159	2528100	2531281	2534464	2537649	2540836
160	2560000	2563201	2566404	2569609	2572816
161	2592100	2595321	2598544	2601769	2604996
162	2624400	2627641	2630884	2634129	2637376
163	2656900	2660161	2663424	2666689	2669956
164	2689600	2692881	2696164	2699449	2702736
165	2722500	2725801	2729104	2732409	2735716
166	2755600	2758921	2762244	2765569	2768896
167	2788900	2792241	2795584	2798929	2802276
168	2822400	2825761	2829124	2832489	2835856
169	2856100	2859481	2862864	2866249	2869636
170	2890000	2893401	2896804	2900209	2903616
171	2924100	2927521	2930944	2934369	2937796
172	2958400	2961841	2965284	2968729	2972176
173	2992900	2996361	2999824	3003289	3006756
174	3027600	3031081	3034564	3038049	3041536
175	3062500	3066001	3069504	3073009	3076516
176	3097600	3101121	3104644	3108169	3111696
177	3132900	3136441	3139984	3143529	3147076
178	3168400	3171961	3175524	3179089	3182656
179	3204100	3207681	3211264	3214849	3218436
180	3240000	3243601	3247204	3250809	3254416
181	3276100	3279721	3283344	3286969	3290596
182	3312400	3316041	3319684	3323329	3326976
183	3348900	3352561	3356224	3359889	3363556
184	3385600	3389281	3392964	3396649	3400336
185	3422500	3426201	3429904	3433609	3437316
186	3459600	3463321	3467044	3470769	3474496
187	3496900	3500641	3504384	3508129	3511876
188	3534400	3538161	3541924	3545689	3549456
189	3572100	3575881	3579664	3583449	3587236
190	3610000	3613801	3617604	3621409	3625216
191	3648100	3651921	3655744	3659569	3663396
192	3686400	3690241	3694084	3697929	3701776
193	3724900	3728761	3732624	3736489	3740356
194	3763600	3767481	3771364	3775249	3779136
195	3802500	3806401	3810304	3814209	3818116
196	3841600	3845521	3849444	3853369	3857296
197	3880900	3884841	3888784	3892729	3896676
198	3920400	3924361	3928324	3932289	3936256
199	3960100	3964081	3968064	3972049	3976036

5	6	7	8	9	n
2265025	2268036	2271049	2274064	2277081	150
2295225	2298256	2301289	2304324	2307361	151
2325625	2328676	2331729	2334784	2337841	152
2356225	2359296	2362369	2365444	2368521	153
2387025	2390116	2393209	2396304	2399401	154
2418025	2421136	2424249	2427364	2430481	155
2449225	2452356	2455489	2458624	2461761	156
2480625	2483776	2486929	2490084	2493241	157
2512225	2515396	2518569	2521744	2524921	158
2544025	2547216	2550409	2553604	2556801	159
2576025	2579236	2582449	2585664	2588881	160
2608225	2611456	2614689	2617924	2621161	161
2640625	2643876	2647129	2650384	2653641	162
2673225	2676496	2679769	2683044	2686321	163
2706025	2709316	2712609	2715904	2719201	164
2739025	2742336	2745649	2748964	2752281	165
2772225	2775556	2778889	2782224	2785561	166
2805625	2808976	2812329	2815684	2819041	167
2839225	2842596	2845969	2849344	2852721	168
2873025	2876416	2879809	2883204	2886601	169
2907025	2910436	2913849	2917264	2920681	170
2941225	2944656	2948089	2951524	2954961	171
2975625	2979076	2982529	2985984	2989441	172
3010225	3013696	3017169	3020644	3024121	173
3045025	3048516	3052009	3055504	3059001	174
3080025	3083536	3087049	3090564	3094081	175
3115225	3118756	3122289	3125824	3129361	176
3150625	3154176	3157729	3161284	3164841	177
3186225	3189796	3193369	3196944	3200521	178
3222025	3225616	3229209	3232804	3236401	179
3258025	3261636	3265249	3268864	3272481	180
3294225	3297856	3301489	3305124	3308761	181
3330625	3334276	3337929	3341584	3345241	182
3367225	3370896	3374569	3378244	3381921	183
3404025	3407716	3411409	3415104	3418801	184
3441025	3444736	3448449	3452164	3455881	185
3478225	3481956	3485689	3489424	3493161	186
3515625	3519376	3523129	3526884	3530641	187
3553225	3556996	3560769	3564544	3568321	188
3591025	3594816	3598609	3602404	3606201	189
3629025	3632836	3636649	3640464	3644281	190
3667225	3671056	3674889	3678724	3682561	191
3705625	3709476	3713329	3717184	3721041	192
3744225	3748096	3751969	3755844	3759721	193
3783025	3786916	3790809	3794704	3798601	194
3822025	3825936	3829849	3833764	3837681	195
3861225	3865156	3869089	3873024	3876961	196
3900625	3904576	3908529	3912484	3916441	197
3940225	3944196	3948169	3952144	3956121	198
3980025	3984016	3988009	3992004	3996001	199

n	0	1	2	3	4
200	4000000	4004001	4008004	4012009	4016016
201	4040100	4044121	4048144	4052169	4056196
202	4080400	4084441	4088484	4092529	4096576
203	4120900	4124961	4129024	4133089	4137156
204	4161600	4165681	4169764	4173849	4177936
205	4202500	4206601	4210704	4214809	4218916
206	4243600	4247721	4251844	4255969	4260096
207	4284900	4289041	4293184	4297329	4301476
208	4326400	4330561	4334724	4338889	4343056
209	4368100	4372281	4376464	4380649	4384836
210	4410000	4414201	4418404	4422609	4426816
211	4452100	4456321	4460544	4464769	4468996
212	4494400	4498641	4502884	4507129	4511376
213	4536900	4541161	4545424	4549689	4553956
214	4579600	4583881	4588164	4592449	4596736
215	4622500	4626801	4631104	4635409	4639716
216	4665600	4669921	4674244	4678569	4682896
217	4708900	4713241	4717584	4721929	4726276
218	4752400	4756761	4761124	4765489	4769856
219	4796100	4800481	4804864	4809249	4813636
220	4840000	4844401	4848804	4853209	4857616
221	4884100	4888521	4892944	4897369	4901796
222	4928400	4932841	4937284	4941729	4946176
223	4972900	4977361	4981824	4986289	4990756
224	5017600	5022081	5026564	5031049	5035536
225	5062500	5067001	5071504	5076009	5080516
226	5107600	5112121	5116644	5121169	5125696
227	5152900	5157441	5161984	5166529	5171076
228	5198400	5202961	5207524	5212089	5216656
229	5244100	5248681	5253264	5257849	5262436
230	5290000	5294601	5299204	5303809	5308416
231	5336100	5340721	5345344	5349969	5354596
232	5382400	5387041	5391684	5396329	5400976
233	5428900	5433561	5438224	5442889	5447556
234	5475600	5480281	5484964	5489649	5494336
235	5522500	5527201	5531904	5536609	5541316
236	5569600	5574321	5579044	5583769	5588496
237	5616900	5621641	5626384	5631129	5635876
238	5664400	5669161	5673924	5678689	5683456
239	5712100	5716881	5721664	5726449	5731236
240	5760000	5764801	5769604	5774409	5779216
241	5808100	5812921	5817744	5822569	5827396
242	5856400	5861241	5866084	5870929	5875776
243	5904900	5909761	5914624	5919489	5924356
244	5953600	5958481	5963364	5968249	5973136
245	6002500	6007401	6012304	6017209	6022116
246	6051600	6056521	6061444	6066369	6071296
247	6100900	6105841	6110784	6115729	6120676
248	6150400	6155361	6160324	6165289	6170256
249	6200100	6205081	6210064	6215049	6220036

5	6	7	8	9	n
4020025	4024036	4028049	4032064	4036081	200
4060225	4064256	4068289	4072324	4076361	201
4100625	4104676	4108729	4112784	4116841	202
4141225	4145296	4149369	4153444	4157521	203
4182025	4186116	4190209	4194304	4198401	204
4223025	4227136	4231249	4235364	4239481	205
4264225	4268356	4272489	4276624	4280761	206
4305625	4309776	4313929	4318084	4322241	207
4347225	4351396	4355569	4359744	4363921	208
4389025	4393216	4397409	4401604	4405801	209
4431025	4435236	4439449	4443664	4447881	210
4473225	4477456	4481689	4485924	4490161	211
4515625	4519876	4524129	4528384	4532641	212
4558225	4562496	4566769	4571044	4575321	213
4601025	4605316	4609609	4613904	4618201	214
4644025	4648336	4652649	4656964	4661281	215
4687225	4691556	4695889	4700224	4704561	216
4730625	4734976	4739329	4743684	4748041	217
4774225	4778596	4782969	4787344	4791721	218
4818025	4822416	4826809	4831204	4835601	219
4862025	4866436	4870849	4875264	4879681	220
4906225	4910656	4915089	4919524	4923961	221
4950625	4955076	4959529	4963984	4968441	222
4995225	4999696	5004169	5008644	5013121	223
5040025	5044516	5049009	5053504	5058001	224
5085025	5089536	5094049	5098564	5103081	225
5130225	5134756	5139289	5143824	5148361	226
5175625	5180176	5184729	5189284	5193841	227
5221225	5225796	5230369	5234944	5239521	228
5267025	5271616	5276209	5280804	5285401	229
5313025	5317636	5322249	5326864	5331481	230
5359225	5363856	5368489	5373124	5377761	231
5405625	5410276	5414929	5419584	5424241	232
5452225	5456896	5461569	5466244	5470921	233
5499025	5503716	5508409	5513104	5517801	234
5546025	5550736	5555449	5560164	5564881	235
5593225	5597956	5602689	5607424	5612161	236
5640625	5645376	5650129	5654884	5659641	237
5688225	5692996	5697769	5702544	5707321	238
5736025	5740816	5745609	5750404	5755201	239
5784025	5788836	5793649	5798464	5803281	240
5832225	5837056	5841889	5846724	5851561	241
5880625	5885476	5890329	5895184	5900041	242
5929225	5934096	5938969	5943844	5948721	243
5978025	5982916	5987809	5992704	5997601	244
6027025	6031936	6036849	6041764	6046681	245
6076225	6081156	6086089	6091024	6095961	246
6125625	6130576	6135529	6140484	6145441	247
6175225	6180196	6185169	6190144	6195121	248
6225025	6230016	6235009	6240004	6245001	249

n	0	1	2	3	4
250	6250000	6255001	6260004	6265009	6270016
251	6300100	6305121	6310144	6315169	6320196
252	6350400	6355441	6360484	6365529	6370576
253	6400900	6405961	6411024	6416089	6421156
254	6451600	6456681	6461764	6466849	6471936
255	6502500	6507601	6512704	6517809	6522916
256	6553600	6558721	6563844	6568969	6574096
257	6604900	6610041	6615184	6620329	6625476
258	6656400	6661561	6666724	6671889	6677056
259	6708100	6713281	6718464	6723649	6728836
260	6760000	6765201	6770404	6775609	6780816
261	6812100	6817321	6822544	6827769	6832996
262	6864400	6869641	6874884	6880129	6885376
263	6916900	6922161	6927424	6932689	6937956
264	6969600	6974881	6980164	6985449	6990736
265	7022500	7027801	7033104	7038409	7043716
266	7075600	7080921	7086244	7091569	7096896
267	7128900	7134241	7139584	7144929	7150276
268	7182400	7187761	7193124	7198489	7203856
269	7236100	7241481	7246864	7252249	7257636
270	7290000	7295401	7300804	7306209	7311616
271	7344100	7349521	7354944	7360369	7365796
272	7398400	7403841	7409284	7414729	7420176
273	7452900	7458361	7463824	7469289	7474756
274	7507600	7513081	7518564	7524049	7529536
275	7562500	7568001	7573504	7579009	7584516
276	7617600	7623121	7628644	7634169	7639696
277	7672900	7678441	7683984	7689529	7695076
278	7728400	7733961	7739524	7745089	7750656
279	7784100	7789681	7795264	7800849	7806436
280	7840000	7845601	7851204	7856809	7862416
281	7896100	7901721	7907344	7912969	7918596
282	7952400	7958041	7963684	7959329	7974976
283	8008900	8014561	8020224	8025889	8031556
284	8065600	8071281	8076964	8082649	8088336
285	8122500	8128201	8133904	8139609	8145316
286	8179600	8185321	8191044	8196769	8202496
287	8236900	8242641	8248384	8254129	8259876
288	8294400	8300161	8305924	8311689	8317456
289	8352100	8357881	8363664	8369449	8375236
290	8410000	8415801	8421604	8427409	8433216
291	8468100	8473921	8479744	8485569	8491396
292	8526400	8532241	8538084	8543929	8549776
293	8584900	8590761	8596624	8602489	8608356
294	8643600	8649481	8655364	8661249	8667136
295	8702500	8708401	8714304	8720209	8726116
296	8761600	8767521	8773444	8779369	8785296
297	8820900	8826841	8832784	8838729	8844676
298	8880400	8886361	8892324	8898289	8904256
299	8940100	8946081	8952064	8958049	8964036

5	6	7	8	9	n
6275025	6280036	6285049	6290064	6295081	250
6325225	6330256	6335289	6340324	6345361	251
6375625	6380676	6385729	6390784	6395841	252
6426225	6431296	6436369	6441444	6446521	253
6477025	6482116	6487209	6492304	6497401	254
6528025	6533136	6538249	6543364	6548481	255
6579225	6584356	6589489	6594624	6599761	256
6630625	6635776	6640929	6646084	6651241	257
6682225	6687396	6692569	6697744	6702921	258
6734025	6739216	6744409	6749604	6754801	259
6786025	6791236	6796449	6801664	6806881	260
6838225	6843456	6848689	6853924	6859161	261
6890625	6895876	6901129	6906384	6911641	262
6943225	6948496	6953769	6959044	6964321	263
6996025	7001316	7006609	7011904	7017201	264
7049025	7054336	7059649	7064964	7070281	265
7102225	7107556	7112889	7118224	7123561	266
7155625	7160976	7166329	7171684	7177041	267
7209225	7214596	7219969	7225344	7230721	268
7263025	7268416	7273809	7279204	7284601	269
7317025	7322436	7327849	7333264	7338681	270
7371225	7376656	7382089	7387524	7392961	271
7425625	7431076	7436529	7441984	7447441	272
7480225	7485696	7491169	7496644	7502121	273
7535025	7540516	7546009	7551504	7557001	274
7590025	7595536	7601049	7606564	7612081	275
7645225	7650756	7656289	7661824	7667361	276
7700625	7706176	7711729	7717284	7722841	277
7756225	7761796	7767369	7772944	7778521	278
7812025	7817616	7823209	7828804	7834401	279
7868025	7873636	7879249	7884864	7890481	280
7924225	7929856	7935489	7941124	7946761	281
7980625	7986276	7991929	7997584	8003241	282
8037225	8042896	8048569	8054244	8059921	283
8094025	8099716	8105409	8111104	8116801	284
8151025	8156736	8162449	8168164	8173881	285
8208225	8213956	8219689	8225424	8231161	286
8265625	8271376	8277129	8282884	8288641	287
8323225	8328996	8334769	8340544	8346321	288
8381025	8386816	8392609	8398404	8404201	289
8439025	8444836	8450649	8456464	8462281	290
8497225	8503056	8508889	8514724	8520561	291
8555625	8561476	8567329	8573184	8579041	292
8614225	8620096	8625969	8631844	8637721	293
8673025	8678916	8684809	8690704	8696601	294
8732025	8737936	8743849	8749764	8755681	295
8791225	8797156	8803089	8809024	8814961	296
8850625	8856576	8862529	8868484	8874441	297
8910225	8916196	8922169	8928144	8934121	298
8970025	8976016	8982009	8988004	8994001	299

n	0	1	2	3	4
300	9000000	9006001	9012004	9018009	9024016
301	9060100	9066121	9072144	9078169	9084196
302	9120400	9126441	9132484	9138529	9144576
303	9180900	9186961	9193024	9199089	9205156
304	9241600	9247681	9253764	9259849	9265936
305	9302500	9308601	9314704	9320809	9326916
306	9363600	9369721	9375844	9381969	9388096
307	9424900	9431041	9437184	9443329	9449476
308	9486400	9492561	9498724	9504889	9511056
309	9548100	9554281	9560464	9566649	9572836
310	9610000	9616201	9622404	9628609	9634816
311	9672100	9678321	9684544	9690769	9696996
312	9734400	9740641	9746884	9753129	9759376
313	9796900	9803161	9809424	9815689	9821956
314	9859600	9865881	9872164	9878449	9884736
315	9922500	9928801	9935104	9941409	9947716
316	9985600	9991921	9998244	10004569	10010896
317	10048900	10055241	10061584	10067929	10074276
318	10112400	10118761	10125124	10131489	10137856
319	10176100	10182481	10188864	10195249	10201636
320	10240000	10246401	10252804	10259209	10265616
321	10304100	10310521	10316944	10323369	10329796
322	10368400	10374841	10381284	10387729	10394176
323	10432900	10439361	10445824	10452289	10458756
324	10497600	10504081	10510564	10517049	10523536
325	10562500	10569001	10575504	10582009	10588516
326	10627600	10634121	10640644	10647169	10653696
327	10692900	10699441	10705984	10712529	10719076
328	10758400	10764961	10771524	10778089	10784656
329	10824100	10830681	10837264	10843849	10850436
330	10890000	10896601	10903204	10909809	10916416
331	10956100	10962721	10969344	10975969	10982596
332	11022400	11029041	11035684	11042329	11048976
333	11088900	11095561	11102224	11108889	11115556
334	11155600	11162281	11168964	11175649	11182336
335	11222500	11229201	11235904	11242609	11249316
336	11289600	11296321	11303044	11309769	11316496
337	11356900	11363641	11370384	11377129	11383876
338	11424400	11431161	11437924	11444689	11451456
339	11492100	11498881	11505664	11512449	11519236
340	11560000	11566801	11573604	11580409	11587216
341	11628100	11634921	11641744	11648569	11655396
342	11696400	11703241	11710084	11716929	11723776
343	11764900	11771761	11778624	11785489	11792356
344	11833600	11840481	11847364	11854249	11861136
345	11902500	11909401	11916304	11923209	11930116
346	11971600	11978521	11985444	11992369	11999296
347	12040900	12047841	12054784	12061729	12068676
348	12110400	12117361	12124324	12131289	12138256
349	12180100	12187081	12194064	12201049	12208036

5	6	7	8	9	n
9030025	9036036	9042049	9048064	9054081	300
9090225	9096256	9102289	9108324	9114361	301
9150625	9156676	9162729	9168784	9174841	302
9211225	9217296	9223369	9229444	9235521	303
9272025	9278116	9284209	9290304	9296401	304
9333025	9339136	9345249	9351364	9357481	305
9394225	9400356	9406489	9412624	9418761	306
9455625	9461776	9467929	9474084	9480241	307
9517225	9523396	9529569	9535744	9541921	308
9579025	9585216	9591409	9597604	9603801	309
9641025	9647236	9653449	9659664	9665881	310
9703225	9709456	9715689	9721924	9728161	311
9765625	9771876	9778129	9784384	9790641	312
9828225	9834496	9840769	9847044	9853321	313
9891025	9897316	9903609	9909904	9916201	314
9954025	9960336	9966649	9972964	9979281	315
10017225	10023556	10029889	10036224	10042561	316
10080625	10086976	10093329	10099684	10106041	317
10144225	10150596	10156969	10163344	10169721	318
10208025	10214416	10220809	10227204	10233601	319
10272025	10278436	10284849	10291264	10297681	320
10336225	10342656	10349089	10355524	10361961	321
10400625	10407076	10413529	10419984	10426441	322
10465225	10471696	10478169	10484644	10491121	323
10530025	10536516	10543009	10549504	10556001	324
10595025	10601536	10608049	10614564	10621081	325
10660225	10666756	10673289	10679824	10686361	326
10725625	10732176	10738729	10745284	10751841	327
10791225	10797796	10804369	10810944	10817521	328
10857025	10863616	10870209	10876804	10883401	329
10923025	10929636	10936249	10942864	10949481	330
10989225	10995856	11002489	11009124	11015761	331
11055625	11062276	11068929	11075584	11082241	332
11122225	11128896	11135569	11142244	11148921	333
11189025	11195716	11202409	11209104	11215801	334
11256025	11262736	11269449	11276164	11282881	335
11323225	11329956	11336689	11343424	11350161	336
11390625	11397376	11404129	11410884	11417641	337
11458225	11464996	11471769	11478544	11485321	338
11526025	11532816	11539609	11546404	11553201	339
11594025	11600836	11607649	11614464	11621281	340
11662225	11669056	11675889	11682724	11689561	341
11730625	11737476	11744329	11751184	11758041	342
11799225	11806096	11812969	11819844	11826721	343
11868025	11874916	11881809	11888704	11895601	344
11937025	11943936	11950849	11957764	11964681	345
12006225	12013156	12020089	12027024	12033961	346
12075625	12082576	12089529	12096484	12103441	347
12145225	12152196	12159169	12166144	12173121	348
12215025	12222016	12229009	12236004	12243001	349

n	0	1	2	3	4
350	12250000	12257001	12264004	12271009	12278016
351	12320100	12327121	12334144	12341169	12348196
352	12390400	12397441	12404484	12411529	12418576
353	12460900	12467961	12475024	12482089	12489156
354	12531600	12538681	12545764	12552849	12559936
355	12602500	12609601	12616704	12623809	12630916
356	12673600	12680721	12687844	12694969	12702096
357	12744900	12752041	12759184	12766329	12773476
358	12816400	12823561	12830724	12837889	12845056
359	12888100	12895281	12902464	12909649	12916836
360	12960000	12967201	12974404	12981609	12988816
361	13032100	13039321	13046544	13053769	13060996
362	13104400	13111641	13118884	13126129	13133376
363	13176900	13184161	13191424	13198689	13205956
364	13249600	13256881	13264164	13271449	13278736
365	13322500	13329801	13337104	13344409	13351716
366	13395600	13402921	13410244	13417569	13424896
367	13468900	13476241	13483584	13490929	13498276
368	13542400	13549761	13557124	13564489	13571856
369	13616100	13623481	13630864	13638249	13645636
370	13690000	13697401	13704804	13712209	13719616
371	13764100	13771521	13778944	13786369	13793796
372	13838400	13845841	13853284	13860729	13868176
373	13912900	13920361	13927824	13935289	13942756
374	13987600	13995081	14002564	14010049	14017536
375	14062500	14070001	14077504	14085009	14092516
376	14137600	14145121	14152644	14160169	14167696
377	14212900	14220441	14227984	14235529	14243076
378	14288400	14295961	14303524	14311089	14318656
379	14364100	14371681	14379264	14386849	14394436
380	14440000	14447601	14455204	14462809	14470416
381	14516100	14523721	14531344	14538969	14546596
382	14592400	14600041	14607684	14615329	14622976
383	14668900	14676561	14684224	14691889	14699556
384	14745600	14753281	14760964	14768649	14776336
385	14822500	14830201	14837904	14845609	14853316
386	14899600	14907321	14915044	14922769	14930496
387	14976900	14984641	14992384	15000129	15007876
388	15054400	15062161	15069924	15077689	15085456
389	15132100	15139881	15147664	15155449	15163236
390	15210000	15217801	15225604	15233409	15241216
391	15288100	15295921	15303744	15311569	15319396
392	15366400	15374241	15382084	15389929	15397776
393	15444900	15452761	15460624	15468489	15476356
394	15523600	15531481	15539364	15547249	15555136
395	15602500	15610401	15618304	15626209	15634116
396	15681600	15689521	15697444	15705369	15713296
397	15760900	15768841	15776784	15784729	15792676
398	15840400	15848361	15856324	15864289	15872256
399	15920100	15928081	15936064	15944049	15952036

5	6	7	8	9	n
12285025	12292036	12299049	12306064	12313081	350
12355225	12362256	12369289	12376324	12383361	351
12425625	12432676	12439729	12446784	12453841	352
12496225	12503296	12510369	12517444	12524521	353
12567025	12574116	12581209	12588304	12595401	354
12638025	12645136	12652249	12659364	12666481	355
12709225	12716356	12723489	12730624	12737761	356
12780625	12787776	12794929	12802084	12809241	357
12852225	12859396	12866569	12873744	12880921	358
12924025	12931216	12938409	12945604	12952801	359
12996025	13003236	13010449	13017664	13024881	360
13068225	13075456	13082689	13089924	13097161	361
13140625	13147876	13155129	13162384	13169641	362
13213225	13220496	13227769	13235044	13242321	363
13286025	13293316	13300609	13307904	13315201	364
13359025	13366336	13373649	13380964	13388281	365
13432225	13439556	13446889	13454224	13461561	366
13505625	13512976	13520329	13527684	13535041	367
13579225	13586596	13593969	13601344	13608721	368
13653025	13660416	13667809	13675204	13682601	369
13727025	13734436	13741849	13749264	13756681	370
13801225	13808656	13816089	13823524	13830961	371
13875625	13883076	13890529	13897984	13905441	372
13950225	13957696	13965169	13972644	13980121	373
14025025	14032516	14040009	14047504	14055001	374
14100025	14107536	14115049	14122564	14130081	375
14175225	14182756	14190289	14197824	14205361	376
14250625	14258176	14265729	14273284	14280841	377
14326225	14333796	14341369	14348944	14356521	378
14402025	14409616	14417209	14424804	14432401	379
14478025	14485636	14493249	14500864	14508481	380
14554225	14561856	14569489	14577124	14584761	381
14630625	14638276	14645929	14653584	14661241	382
14707225	14714896	14722569	14730244	14737921	383
14784025	14791716	14799409	14807104	14814801	384
14861025	14868736	14876449	14884164	14891881	385
14938225	14945956	14953689	14961424	14969161	386
15015625	15023376	15031129	15038884	15046641	387
15093225	15100996	15108769	15116544	15124321	388
15171025	15178816	15186609	15194404	15202201	389
15249025	15256836	15264649	15272464	15280281	390
15327225	15335056	15342889	15350724	15358561	391
15405625	15413476	15421329	15429184	15437041	392
15484225	15492096	15499969	15507844	15515721	393
15563025	15570916	15578809	15586704	15594601	394
15642025	15649936	15657849	15665764	15673681	395
15721225	15729156	15737089	15745024	15752961	396
15800625	15808576	15816529	15824484	15832441	397
15880225	15888196	15896169	15904144	15912121	398
15960025	15968016	15976009	15984004	15992001	399

n	0	1	2	3	4
400	16000000	16008001	16016004	16024009	16032016
401	16080100	16088121	16096144	16104169	16112196
402	16160400	16168441	16176484	16184529	16192576
403	16240900	16248961	16257024	16265089	16273156
404	16321600	16329681	16337764	16345849	16353936
405	16402500	16410601	16418704	16426809	16434916
406	16483600	16491721	16499844	16507969	16516096
407	16564900	16573041	16581184	16589329	16597476
408	16646400	16654561	16662724	16670889	16679056
409	16728100	16736281	16744464	16752649	16760836
410	16810000	16818201	16826404	16834609	16842816
411	16892100	16900321	16908544	16916769	16924996
412	16974400	16982641	16990884	16999129	17007376
413	17056900	17065161	17073424	17081689	17089956
414	17139600	17147881	17156164	17164449	17172736
415	17222500	17230801	17239104	17247409	17255716
416	17305600	17313921	17322244	17330569	17338896
417	17388900	17397241	17405584	17413929	17422276
418	17472400	17480761	17489124	17497489	17505856
419	17556100	17564481	17572864	17581249	17589636
420	17640000	17648401	17656804	17665209	17673616
421	17724100	17732521	17740944	17749369	17757796
422	17808400	17816841	17825284	17833729	17842176
423	17892900	17901361	17909824	17918289	17926756
424	17977600	17986081	17994564	18003049	18011536
425	18062500	18071001	18079504	18088009	18096516
426	18147600	18156121	18164644	18173169	18181696
427	18232900	18241441	18249984	18258529	18267076
428	18318400	18326961	18335524	18344089	18352656
429	18404100	18412681	18421264	18429849	18438436
430	18490000	18498601	18507204	18515809	18524416
431	18576100	18584721	18593344	18601969	18610596
432	18662400	18671041	18679684	18688329	18696976
433	18748900	18757561	18766224	18774889	18783556
434	18835600	18844281	18852964	18861649	18870336
435	18922500	18931201	18939904	18948609	18957316
436	19009600	19018321	19027044	19035769	19044496
437	19096900	19105641	19114384	19123129	19131876
438	19184400	19193161	19201924	19210689	19219456
439	19272100	19280881	19289664	19298449	19307236
440	19360000	19368801	19377604	19386409	19395216
441	19448100	19456921	19465744	19474569	19483396
442	19536400	19545241	19554084	19562929	19571776
443	19624900	19633761	19642624	19651489	19660356
444	19713600	19722481	19731364	19740249	19749136
445	19802500	19811401	19820304	19829209	19838116
446	19891600	19900521	19909444	19918369	19927296
447	19980900	19989841	19998784	20007729	20016676
448	20070400	20079361	20088324	20097289	20106256
449	20160100	20169081	20178064	20187049	20196036

5	6	7	8	9	n
16040025	16048036	16056049	16064064	16072081	400
16120225	16128256	16136289	16144324	16152361	401
16200625	16208676	16216729	16224784	16232841	402
16281225	16289296	16297369	16305444	16313521	403
16362025	16370116	16378209	16386304	16394401	404
16443025	16451136	16459249	16467364	16475481	405
16524225	16532356	16540489	16548624	16556761	406
16605625	16613776	16621929	16630084	16638241	407
16687225	16695396	16703569	16711744	16719921	408
16769025	16777216	16785409	16793604	16801801	409
16851025	16859236	16867449	16875664	16883881	410
16933225	16941456	16949689	16957924	16966161	411
17015625	17023876	17032129	17040384	17048641	412
17098225	17106496	17114769	17123044	17131321	413
17181025	17189316	17197609	17205904	17214201	414
17264025	17272336	17280649	17288964	17297281	415
17347225	17355556	17363889	17372224	17380561	416
17430625	17438976	17447329	17455684	17464041	417
17514225	17522596	17530969	17539344	17547721	418
17598025	17606416	17614809	17623204	17631601	419
17682025	17690436	17698849	17707264	17715681	420
17766225	17774656	17783089	17791524	17799961	421
17850625	17859076	17867529	17875984	17884441	422
17935225	17943696	17952169	17960644	17969121	423
18020025	18028516	18037009	18045504	18054001	424
18105025	18113536	18122049	18130564	18139081	425
18190225	18198756	18207289	18215824	18224361	426
18275625	18284176	18292729	18301284	18309841	427
18361225	18369796	18378369	18386944	18395521	428
18447025	18455616	18464209	18472804	18481401	429
18533025	18541636	18550249	18558864	18567481	430
18619225	18627856	18636489	18645124	18653761	431
18705625	18714276	18722929	18731584	18740241	432
18792225	18800896	18809569	18818244	18826921	433
18879025	18887716	18896409	18905104	18913801	434
18966025	18974736	18983449	18992164	19000881	435
19053225	19061956	19070689	19079424	19088161	436
19140625	19149376	19158129	19166884	19175641	437
19228225	19236996	19245769	19254544	19263321	438
19316025	19324816	19333609	19342404	19351201	439
19404025	19412836	19421649	19430464	19439281	440
19492225	19501056	19509889	19518724	19527561	441
19580625	19589476	19598329	19607184	19616041	442
19669225	19678096	19686969	19695844	19704721	443
19758025	19766916	19775809	19784704	19793601	444
19847025	19855936	19864849	19873764	19882681	445
19936225	19945156	19954089	19963024	19971961	446
20025625	20034576	20043529	20052484	20061441	447
20115225	20124196	20133169	20142144	20151121	448
20205025	20214016	20223009	20232004	20241001	449

n	0	1	2	3	4
450	20250000	20259001	20268004	20277009	20286016
451	20340100	20349121	20358144	20367169	20376196
452	20430400	20439441	20448484	20457529	20466576
453	20520900	20529961	20539024	20548089	20557156
454	20611600	20620681	20629764	20638849	20647936
455	20702500	20711601	20720704	20729809	20738916
456	20793600	20802721	20811844	20820969	20830096
457	20884900	20894041	20903184	20912329	20921476
458	20976400	20985561	20994724	21003889	21013056
459	21068100	21077281	21086464	21095649	21104836
460	21160000	21169201	21178404	21187609	21196816
461	21252100	21261321	21270544	21279769	21288996
462	21344400	21353641	21362884	21372129	21381376
463	21436900	21446161	21455424	21464689	21473956
464	21529600	21538881	21548164	21557449	21566736
465	21622500	21631801	21641104	21650409	21659716
466	21715600	21724921	21734244	21743569	21752896
467	21808900	21818241	21827584	21836929	21846276
468	21902400	21911761	21921124	21930489	21939856
469	21996100	22005481	22014864	22024249	22033636
470	22090000	22099401	22108804	22118209	22127616
471	22184100	22193521	22202944	22212369	22221796
472	22278400	22287841	22297284	22306729	22316176
473	22372900	22382361	22391824	22401289	22410756
474	22467600	22477081	22486564	22496049	22505536
475	22562500	22572001	22581504	22591009	22600516
476	22657600	22667121	22676644	22686169	22695696
477	22752900	22762441	22771984	22781529	22791076
478	22848400	22857961	22867524	22877089	22886656
479	22944100	22953681	22963264	22972849	22982436
480	23040000	23049601	23059204	23068809	23078416
481	23136100	23145721	23155344	23164969	23174596
482	23232400	23242041	23251684	23261329	23270976
483	23328900	23338561	23348224	23357889	23367556
484	23425600	23435281	23444964	23454649	23464336
485	23522500	23532201	23541904	23551609	23561316
486	23619600	23629321	23639044	23648769	23658496
487	23716900	23726641	23736384	23746129	23755876
488	23814400	23824161	23833924	23843689	23853456
489	23912100	23921881	23931664	23941449	23951236
490	24010000	24019801	24029604	24039409	24049216
491	24108100	24117921	24127744	24137569	24147396
492	24206400	24216241	24226084	24235929	24245776
493	24304900	24314761	24324624	24334489	24344356
494	24403600	24413481	24423364	24433249	24443136
495	24502500	24512401	24522304	24532209	24542116
496	24601600	24611521	24621444	24631369	24641296
497	24700900	24710841	24720784	24730729	24740676
498	24800400	24810361	24820324	24830289	24840256
499	24900100	24910081	24920064	24930049	24940036

5	6	7	8	9	n
20295025	20304036	20313049	20322064	20331081	450
20385225	20394256	20403289	20412324	20421361	451
20475625	20484676	20493729	20502784	20511841	452
20566225	20575296	20584369	20593444	20602521	453
20657025	20666116	20675209	20684304	20693401	454
20748025	20757136	20766249	20775364	20784481	455
20839225	20848356	20857489	20866624	20875761	456
20930625	20939776	20948929	20958084	20967241	457
21022225	21031396	21040569	21049744	21058921	458
21114025	21123216	21132409	21141604	21150801	459
21206025	21215236	21224449	21233664	21242881	460
21298225	21307456	21316689	21325924	21335161	461
21390625	21399876	21409129	21418384	21427641	462
21483225	21492496	21501769	21511044	21520321	463
21576025	21585316	21594609	21603904	21613201	464
21669025	21678336	21687649	21696964	21706281	465
21762225	21771556	21780889	21790224	21799561	466
21855625	21864976	21874329	21883684	21893041	467
21949225	21958596	21967969	21977344	21986721	468
22043025	22052416	22061809	22071204	22080601	469
22137025	22146436	22155849	22165264	22174681	470
22231225	22240656	22250089	22259524	22268961	471
22325625	22335076	22344529	22353984	22363441	472
22420225	22429696	22439169	22448644	22458121	473
22515025	22524516	22534009	22543504	22553001	474
22610025	22619536	22629049	22638564	22648081	475
22705225	22714756	22724289	22733824	22743361	476
22800625	22810176	22819729	22829284	22838841	477
22896225	22905796	22915369	22924944	22934521	478
22992025	23001616	23011209	23020804	23030401	479
23088025	23097636	23107249	23116864	23126481	480
23184225	23193856	23203489	23213124	23222761	481
23280625	23290276	23299929	23309584	23319241	482
23377225	23386896	23396569	23406244	23415921	483
23474025	23483716	23493409	23503104	23512801	484
23571025	23580736	23590449	23600164	23609881	485
23668225	23677956	23687689	23697424	23707161	486
23765625	23775376	23785129	23794884	23804641	487
23863225	23872996	23882769	23892544	23902321	488
23961025	23970816	23980609	23990404	24000201	489
24059025	24068836	24078649	24088464	24098281	490
24157225	24167056	24176889	24186724	24196561	491
24255625	24265476	24275329	24285184	24295041	492
24354225	24364096	24373969	24383844	24393721	493
24453025	24462916	24472809	24482704	24492601	494
24552025	24561936	24571849	24581764	24591681	495
24651225	24661156	24671089	24681024	24690961	496
24750625	24760576	24770529	24780484	24790441	497
24850225	24860196	24870169	24880144	24890121	498
24950025	24960016	24970009	24980004	24990001	499

n	0	1	2	3	4
500	25000000	25010001	25020004	25030009	25040016
501	25100100	25110121	25120144	25130169	25140196
502	25200400	25210441	25220484	25230529	25240576
503	25300900	25310961	25321024	25331089	25341156
504	25401600	25411681	25421764	25431849	25441936
505	25502500	25512601	25522704	25532809	25542916
506	25603600	25613721	25623844	25633969	25644096
507	25704900	25715041	25725184	25735329	25745476
508	25806400	25816561	25826724	25836889	25847056
509	25908100	25918281	25928464	25938649	25948836
510	26010000	26020201	26030404	26040609	26050816
511	26112100	26122321	26132544	26142769	26152996
512	26214400	26224641	26234884	26245129	26255376
513	26316900	26327161	26337424	26347689	26357956
514	26419600	26429881	26440164	26450449	26460736
515	26522500	26532801	26543104	26553409	26563716
516	26625600	26635921	26646244	26656569	26666896
517	26728900	26739241	26749584	26759929	26770276
518	26832400	26842761	26853124	26863489	26873856
519	26936100	26946481	26956864	26967249	26977636
520	27040000	27050401	27060804	27071209	27081616
521	27144100	27154521	27164944	27175369	27185796
522	27248400	27258841	27269284	27279729	27290176
523	27352900	27363361	27373824	27384289	27394756
524	27457600	27468081	27478564	27489049	27499536
525	27562500	27573001	27583504	27594009	27604516
526	27667600	27678121	27688644	27699169	27709696
527	27772900	27783441	27793984	27804529	27815076
528	27878400	27888961	27899524	27910089	27920656
529	27984100	27994681	28005264	28015849	28026436
530	28090000	28100601	28111204	28121809	28132416
531	28196100	28206721	28217344	28227969	28238596
532	28302400	28313041	28323684	28334329	28344976
533	28408900	28419561	28430224	28440889	28451556
534	28515600	28526281	28536964	28547649	28558336
535	28622500	28633201	28643904	28654609	28665316
536	28729600	28740321	28751044	28761769	28772496
537	28836900	28847641	28858384	28869129	28879876
538	28944400	28955161	28965924	28976689	28987456
539	29052100	29062881	29073664	29084449	29095236
540	29160000	29170801	29181604	29192409	29203216
541	29268100	29278921	29289744	29300569	29311396
542	29376400	29387241	29398084	29408929	29419776
543	29484900	29495761	29506624	29517489	29528356
544	29593600	29604481	29615364	29626249	29637136
545	29702500	29713401	29724304	29735209	29746116
546	29811600	29822521	29833444	29844369	29855296
547	29920900	29931841	29942784	29953729	29964676
548	30030400	30041361	30052324	30063289	30074256
549	30140100	30151081	30162064	30173049	30184036

5	6	7	8	9	n
25050025	25060036	25070049	25080064	25090081	500
25150225	25160256	25170289	25180324	25190361	501
25250625	25260676	25270729	25280784	25290841	502
25351225	25361296	25371369	25381444	25391521	503
25452025	25462116	25472209	25482304	25492401	504
25553025	25563136	25573249	25583364	25593481	505
25654225	25664356	25674489	25684624	25694761	506
25755625	25765776	25775929	25786084	25796241	507
25857225	25867396	25877569	25887744	25897921	508
25959025	25969216	25979409	25989604	25999801	509
26061025	26071236	26081449	26091664	26101881	510
26163225	26173456	26183689	26193924	26204161	511
26265625	26275876	26286129	26296384	26306641	512
26368225	26378496	26388769	26399044	26409321	513
26471025	26481316	26491609	26501904	26512201	514
26574025	26584336	26594649	26604964	26615281	515
26677225	26687556	26697889	26708224	26718561	516
26780625	26790976	26801329	26811684	26822041	517
26884225	26894596	26904969	26915344	26925721	518
26988025	26998416	27008809	27019204	27029601	519
27092025	27102436	27112849	27123264	27133681	520
27196225	27206656	27217089	27227524	27237961	521
27300625	27311076	27321529	27331984	27342441	522
27405225	27415696	27426169	27436644	27447121	523
27510025	27520516	27531009	27541504	27552001	524
27615025	27625536	27636049	27646564	27657081	525
27720225	27730756	27741289	27751824	27762361	526
27825625	27836176	27846729	27857284	27867841	527
27931225	27941796	27952369	27962944	27973521	528
28037025	28047616	28058209	28068804	28079401	529
28143025	28153636	28164249	28174864	28185481	530
28249225	28259856	28270489	28281124	28291761	531
28355625	28366276	28376929	28387584	28398241	532
28462225	28472896	28483569	28494244	28504921	533
28569025	28579716	28590409	28601104	28611801	534
28676025	28686736	28697449	28708164	28718881	535
28783225	28793956	28804689	28815424	28826161	536
28890625	28901376	28912129	28922884	28933641	537
28998225	29008996	29019769	29030544	29041321	538
29106025	29116816	29127609	29138404	29149201	539
29214025	29224836	29235649	29246464	29257281	540
29322225	29333056	29343889	29354724	29365561	541
29430625	29441476	29452329	29463184	29474041	542
29539225	29550096	29560969	29571844	29582721	543
29648025	29658916	29669809	29680704	29691601	544
29757025	29767936	29778849	29789764	29800681	545
29866225	29877156	29888089	29899024	29909961	546
29975625	29986576	29997529	30008484	30019441	547
30085225	30096196	30107169	30118144	30129121	548
30195025	30206016	30217009	30228004	30239001	549

n	0	1	2	3	4
550	30250000	30261001	30272004	30283009	30294016
551	30360100	30371121	30382144	30393169	30404196
552	30470400	30481441	30492484	30503529	30514576
553	30580900	30591961	30603024	30614089	30625156
554	30691600	30702681	30713764	30724849	30735936
555	30802500	30813601	30824704	30835809	30846916
556	30913600	30924721	30935844	30946969	30958096
557	31024900	31036041	31047184	31058329	31069476
558	31136400	31147561	31158724	31169889	31181056
559	31248100	31259281	31270464	31281649	31292836
560	31360000	31371201	31382404	31393609	31404816
561	31472100	31483321	31494544	31505769	31516996
562	31584400	31595641	31606884	31618129	31629376
563	31696900	31708161	31719424	31730689	31741956
564	31809600	31820881	31832164	31843449	31854736
565	31922500	31933801	31945104	31956409	31967716
566	32035600	32046921	32058244	32069569	32080896
567	32148900	32160241	32171584	32182929	32194276
568	32262400	32273761	32285124	32296489	32307856
569	32376100	32387481	32398864	32410249	32421636
570	32490000	32501401	32512804	32524209	32535616
571	32604100	32615521	32626944	32638369	32649796
572	32718400	32729841	32741284	32752729	32764176
573	32832900	32844361	32855824	32867289	32878756
574	32947600	32959081	32970564	32982049	32993536
575	33062500	33074001	33085504	33097009	33108516
576	33177600	33189121	33200644	33212169	33223696
577	33292900	33304441	33315984	33327529	33339076
578	33408400	33419961	33431524	33443089	33454656
579	33524100	33535681	33547264	33558849	33570436
580	33640000	33651601	33663204	33674809	33686416
581	33756100	33767721	33779344	33790969	33802596
582	33872400	33884041	33895684	33907329	33918976
583	33988900	34000561	34012224	34023889	34035556
584	34105600	34117281	34128964	34140649	34152336
585	34222500	34234201	34245904	34257609	34269316
586	34339600	34351321	34363044	34374769	34386496
587	34456900	34468641	34480384	34492129	34503876
588	34574400	34586161	34597924	34609689	34621456
589	34692100	34703881	34715664	34727449	34739236
590	34810000	34821801	34833604	34845409	34857216
591	34928100	34939921	34951744	34963569	34975396
592	35046400	35058241	35070084	35081929	35093776
593	35164900	35176761	35188624	35200489	35212356
594	35283600	35295481	35307364	35319249	35331136
595	35402500	35414401	35426304	35438209	35450116
596	35521600	35533521	35545444	35557369	35569296
597	35640900	35652841	35664784	35676729	35688676
598	35760400	35772361	35784324	35796289	35808256
599	35880100	35892081	35904064	35916049	35928036

5	6	7	8	9	n
30305025	30316036	30327049	30338064	30349081	550
30415225	30426256	30437289	30448324	30459361	551
30525625	30536676	30547729	30558784	30569841	552
30636225	30647296	30658369	30669444	30680521	553
30747025	30758116	30769209	30780304	30791401	554
30858025	30869136	30880249	30891364	30902481	555
30969225	30980356	30991489	31002624	31013761	556
31080625	31091776	31102929	31114084	31125241	557
31192225	31203396	31214569	31225744	31236921	558
31304025	31315216	31326409	31337604	31348801	559
31416025	31427236	31438449	31449664	31460881	560
31528225	31539456	31550689	31561924	31573161	561
31640625	31651876	31663129	31674384	31685641	562
31753225	31764496	31775769	31787044	31798321	563
31866025	31877316	31888609	31899904	31911201	564
31979025	31990336	32001649	32012964	32024281	565
32092225	32103556	32114889	32126224	32137561	566
32205625	32216976	32228329	32239684	32251041	567
32319225	32330596	32341969	32353344	32364721	568
32433025	32444416	32455809	32467204	32478601	569
32547025	32558436	32569849	32581264	32592681	570
32661225	32672656	32684089	32695524	32706961	571
32775625	32787076	32798529	32809984	32821441	572
32890225	32901696	32913169	32924644	32936121	573
33005025	33016516	33028009	33039504	33051001	574
33120025	33131536	33143049	33154564	33166081	575
33235225	33246756	33258289	33269824	33281361	576
33350625	33362176	33373729	33385284	33396841	577
33466225	33477796	33489369	33500944	33512521	578
33582025	33593616	33605209	33616804	33628401	579
33698025	33709636	33721249	33732864	33744481	580
33814225	33825856	33837489	33849124	33860761	581
33930625	33942276	33953929	33965584	33977241	582
34047225	34058896	34070569	34082244	34093921	583
34164025	34175716	34187409	34199104	34210801	584
34281025	34292736	34304449	34316164	34327881	585
34398225	34409956	34421689	34433424	34445161	586
34515625	34527376	34539129	34550884	34562641	587
34633225	34644996	34656769	34668544	34680321	588
34751025	34762816	34774609	34786404	34798201	589
34869025	34880836	34892649	34904464	34916281	590
34987225	34999056	35010889	35022724	35034561	591
35105625	35117476	35129329	35141184	35153041	592
35224225	35236096	35247969	35259844	35271721	593
35343025	35354916	35366809	35378704	35390601	594
35462025	35473936	35485849	35497764	35509681	595
35581225	35593156	35605089	35617024	35628961	596
35700625	35712576	35724529	35736484	35748441	597
35820225	35832196	35844169	35856144	35868121	598
35940025	35952016	35964009	35976004	35988001	599

n	0	1	2	3	4
600	36000000	36012001	36024004	36036009	36048016
601	36120100	36132121	36144144	36156169	36168196
602	36240400	36252441	36264484	36276529	36288576
603	36360900	36372961	36385024	36397089	36409156
604	36481600	36493681	36505764	36517849	36529936
605	36602500	36614601	36626704	36638809	36650916
606	36723600	36735721	36747844	36759969	36772096
607	36844900	36857041	36869184	36881329	36893476
608	36966400	36978561	36990724	37002889	37015056
609	37088100	37100281	37112464	37124649	37136836
610	37210000	37222201	37234404	37246609	37258816
611	37332100	37344321	37356544	37368769	37380996
612	37454400	37466641	37478884	37491129	37503376
613	37576900	37589161	37601424	37613689	37625956
614	37699600	37711881	37724164	37736449	37748736
615	37822500	37834801	37847104	37859409	37871716
616	37945600	37957921	37970244	37982569	37994896
617	38068900	38081241	38093584	38105929	38118276
618	38192400	38204761	38217124	38229489	38241856
619	38316100	38328481	38340864	38353249	38365636
620	38440000	38452401	38464804	38477209	38489616
621	38564100	38576521	38588944	38601369	38613796
622	38688400	38700841	38713284	38725729	38738176
623	38812900	38825361	38837824	38850289	38862756
624	38937600	38950081	38962564	38975049	38987536
625	39062500	39075001	39087504	39100009	39112516
626	39187600	39200121	39212644	39225169	39237696
627	39312900	39325441	39337984	39350529	39363076
628	39438400	39450961	39463524	39476089	39488656
629	39564100	39576681	39589264	39601849	39614436
630	39690000	39702601	39715204	39727809	39740416
631	39816100	39828721	39841344	39853969	39866596
632	39942400	39955041	39967684	39980329	39992976
633	40068900	40081561	40094224	40106889	40119556
634	40195600	40208281	40220964	40233649	40246336
635	40322500	40335201	40347904	40360609	40373316
636	40449600	40462321	40475044	40487769	40500496
637	40576900	40589641	40602384	40615129	40627876
638	40704400	40717161	40729924	40742689	40755456
639	40832100	40844881	40857664	40870449	40883236
640	40960000	40972801	40985604	40998409	41011216
641	41088100	41100921	41113744	41126569	41139396
642	41216400	41229241	41242084	41254929	41267776
643	41344900	41357761	41370624	41383489	41396356
644	41473600	41486481	41499364	41512249	41525136
645	41602500	41615401	41628304	41641209	41654116
646	41731600	41744521	41757444	41770369	41783296
647	41860900	41873841	41886784	41899729	41912676
648	41990400	42003361	42016324	42029289	42042256
649	42120100	42133081	42146064.	42159049	42172036

5	6	7	8	9	n
36060025	36072036	36084049	36096064	36108081	600
36180225	36192256	36204289	36216324	36228361	601
36300625	36312676	36324729	36336784	36348841	602
36421225	36433296	36445369	36457444	36469521	603
36542025	36554116	36566209	36578304	36590401	604
36663025	36675136	36687249	36699364	36711481	605
36784225	36796356	36808489	36820624	36832761	606
36905625	36917776	36929929	36942084	36954241	607
37027225	37039396	37051569	37063744	37075921	608
37149025	37161216	37173409	37185604	37197801	609
37271025	37283236	37295449	37307664	37319881	610
37393225	37405456	37417689	37429924	37442161	611
37515625	37527876	37540129	37552384	37564641	612
37638225	37650496	37662769	37675044	37687321	613
37761025	37773316	37785609	37797904	37810201	614
37884025	37896336	37908649	37920964	37933281	615
38007225	38019556	38031889	38044224	38056561	616
38130625	38142976	38155329	38167684	38180041	617
38254225	38266596	38278969	38291344	38303721	618
38378025	38390416	38402809	38415204	38427601	619
38502025	38514436	38526849	38539264	38551681	620
38626225	38638656	38651089	38663524	38675961	621
38750625	38763076	38775529	38787984	38800441	622
38875225	38887696	38900169	38912644	38925121	623
39000025	39012516	39025009	39037504	39050001	624
39125025	39137536	39150049	39162564	39175081	625
39250225	39262756	39275289	39287824	39300361	626
39375625	39388176	39400729	39413284	39425841	627
39501225	39513796	39526369	39538944	39551521	628
39627025	39639616	39652209	39664804	39677401	629
39753025	39765636	39778249	39790864	39803481	630
39879225	39891856	39904489	39917124	39929761	631
40005625	40018276	40030929	40043584	40056241	632
40132225	40144896	40157569	40170244	40182921	633
40259025	40271716	40284409	40297104	40309801	634
40386025	40398736	40411449	40424164	40436881	635
40513225	40525956	40538689	40551424	40564161	636
40640625	40653376	40666129	40678884	40691641	637
40768225	40780996	40793769	40806544	40819321	638
40896025	40908816	40921609	40934404	40947201	639
41024025	41036836	41049649	41062464	41075281	640
41152225	41165056	41177889	41190724	41203561	641
41280625	41293476	41306329	41319184	41332041	642
41409225	41422096	41434969	41447844	41460721	643
41538025	41550916	41563809	41576704	41589601	644
41667025	41679936	41692849	41705764	41718681	645
41796225	41809156	41822089	41835024	41847961	646
41925625	41938576	41951529	41964484	41977441	647
42055225	42068196	42081169	42094144	42107121	648
42185025	42198016	42211009	42224004	42237001	649

n	0	1	2	3	4
650	42250000	42263001	42276004	42289009	42302016
651	42380100	42393121	42406144	42419169	42432196
652	42510400	42523441	42536484	42549529	42562576
653	42640900	42653961	42667024	42680089	42693156
654	42771600	42784681	42797764	42810849	42823936
655	42902500	42915601	42928704	42941809	42954916
656	43033600	43046721	43059844	43072969	43086096
657	43164900	43178041	43191184	43204329	43217476
658	43296400	43309561	43322724	43335889	43349056
659	43428100	43441281	43454464	43467649	43480836
660	43560000	43573201	43586404	43599609	43612816
661	43692100	43705321	43718544	43731769	43744996
662	43824400	43837641	43850884	43864129	43877376
663	43956900	43970161	43983424	43996689	44009956
664	44089600	44102881	44116164	44129449	44142736
665	44222500	44235801	44249104	44262409	44275716
666	44355600	44368921	44382244	44395569	44408896
667	44488900	44502241	44515584	44528929	44542276
668	44622400	44635761	44649124	44662489	44675856
669	44756100	44769481	44782864	44796249	44809636
670	44890000	44903401	44916804	44930209	44943616
671	45024100	45037521	45050944	45064369	45077796
672	45158400	45171841	45185284	45198729	45212176
673	45292900	45306361	45319824	45333289	45346756
674	45427600	45441081	45454564	45468049	45481536
675	45562500	45576001	45589504	45603009	45616516
676	45697600	45711121	45724644	45738169	45751696
677	45832900	45846441	45859984	45873529	45887076
678	45968400	45981961	45995524	46009089	46022656
679	46104100	46117681	46131264	46144849	46158436
680	46240000	46253601	46267204	46280809	46294416
681	46376100	46389721	46403344	46416969	46430596
682	46512400	46526041	46539684	46553329	46566976
683	46648900	46662561	46676224	46689889	46703556
684	46785600	46799281	46812964	46826649	46840336
685	46922500	46936201	46949904	46963609	46977316
686	47059600	47073321	47087044	47100769	47114496
687	47196900	47210641	47224384	47238129	47251876
688	47334400	47348161	47361924	47375689	47389456
689	47472100	47485881	47499664	47513449	47527236
690	47610000	47623801	47637604	47651409	47665216
691	47748100	47761921	47775744	47789569	47803396
692	47886400	47900241	47914084	47927929	47941776
693	48024900	48038761	48052624	48066489	48080356
694	48163600	48177481	48191364	48205249	48219136
695	48302500	48316401	48330304	48344209	48358116
696	48441600	48455521	48469444	48483369	48497296
697	48580900	48594841	48608784	48622729	48636676
698	48720400	48734361	48748324	48762289	48776256
699	48860100	48874081	48888064	48902049	48916036

5	6	7	8	9	n
42315025	42328036	42341049	42354064	42367081	650
42445225	42458256	42471289	42484324	42497361	651
42575625	42588676	42601729	42614784	42627841	652
42706225	42719296	42732369	42745444	42758521	653
42837025	42850116	42863209	42876304	42889401	654
42968025	42981136	42994249	43007364	43020481	655
43099225	43112356	43125489	43138624	43151761	656
43230625	43243776	43256929	43270084	43283241	657
43362225	43375396	43388569	43401744	43414921	658
43494025	43507216	43520409	43533604	43546801	659
43626025	43639236	43652449	43665664	43678881	660
43758225	43771456	43784689	43797924	43811161	661
43890625	43903876	43917129	43930384	43943641	662
44023225	44036496	44049769	44063044	44076321	663
44156025	44169316	44182609	44195904	44209201	664
44289025	44302336	44315649	44328964	44342281	665
44422225	44435556	44448889	44462224	44475561	666
44555625	44568976	44582329	44595684	44609041	667
44689225	44702596	44715969	44729344	44742721	668
44823025	44836416	44849809	44863204	44876601	669
44957025	44970436	44983849	44997264	45010681	670
45091225	45104656	45118089	45131524	45144961	671
45225625	45239076	45252529	45265984	45279441	672
45360225	45373696	45387169	45400644	45414121	673
45495025	45508516	45522009	45535504	45549001	674
45630025	45643536	45657049	45670564	45684081	675
45765225	45778756	45792289	45805824	45819361	676
45900625	45914176	45927729	45941284	45954841	677
46036225	46049796	46063369	46076944	46090521	678
46172025	46185616	46199209	46212804	46226401	679
46308025	46321636	46335249	46348864	46362481	680
46444225	46457856	46471489	46485124	46498761	681
46580625	46594276	46607929	46621584	46635241	682
46717225	46730896	46744569	46758244	46771921	683
46854025	46867716	46881409	46895104	46908801	684
46991025	47004736	47018449	47032164	47045881	685
47128225	47141956	47155689	47169424	47183161	686
47265625	47279376	47293129	47306884	47320641	687
47403225	47416996	47430769	47444544	47458321	688
47541025	47554816	47568609	47582404	47596201	689
47679025	47692836	47706649	47720464	47734281	690
47817225	47831056	47844889	47858724	47872561	691
47955625	47969476	47983329	47997184	48011041	692
48094225	48108096	48121969	48135844	48149721	693
48233025	48246916	48260809	48274704	48288601	694
48372025	48385936	48399849	48413764	48427681	695
48511225	48525156	48539089	48553024	48566961	696
48650625	48664576	48678529	48692484	48706441	697
48790225	48804196	48818169	48832144	48846121	698
48930025	48944016	48958009	48972004	48986001	699

n	0	1	2	3	4
700	49000000	49014001	49028004	49042009	49056016
701	49140100	49154121	49168144	49182169	49196196
702	49280400	49294441	49308484	49322529	49336576
703	49420900	49434961	49449024	49463089	49477156
704	49561600	49575681	49589764	49603849	49617936
705	49702500	49716601	49730704	49744809	49758916
706	49843600	49857721	49871844	49885969	49900096
707	49984900	49999041	50013184	50027329	50041476
708	50126400	50140561	50154724	50168889	50183056
709	50268100	50282281	50296464	50310649	50324836
710	50410000	50424201	50438404	50452609	50466816
711	50552100	50566321	50580544	50594769	50608996
712	50694400	50708641	50722884	50737129	50751376
713	50836900	50851161	50865424	50879689	50893956
714	50979600	50993881	51008164	51022449	51036736
715	51122500	51136801	51151104	51165409	51179716
716	51265600	51279921	51294244	51308569	51322896
717	51408900	51423241	51437584	51451929	51466276
718	51552400	51566761	51581124	51595489	51609856
719	51696100	51710481	51724864	51739249	51753636
720	51840000	51854401	51868804	51883209	51897616
721	51984100	51998521	52012944	52027369	52041796
722	52128400	52142841	52157284	52171729	52186176
723	52272900	52287361	52301824	52316289	52330756
724	52417600	52432081	52446564	52461049	52475536
725	52562500	52577001	52591504	52606009	52620516
726	52707600	52722121	52736644	52751169	52765696
727	52852900	52867441	52881984	52896529	52911076
728	52998400	53012961	53027524	53042089	53056656
729	53144100	53158681	53173264	53187849	53202436
730	53290000	53304601	53319204	53333809	53348416
731	53436100	53450721	53465344	53479969	53494596
732	53582400	53597041	53611684	53626329	53640976
733	53728900	53743561	53758224	53772889	53787556
734	53875600	53890281	53904964	53919649	53934336
735	54022500	54037201	54051904	54066609	54081316
736	54169600	54184321	54199044	54213769	54228496
737	54316900	54331641	54346384	54361129	54375876
738	54464400	54479161	54493924	54508689	54523456
739	54612100	54626881	54641664	54656449	54671236
740	54760000	54774801	54789604	54804409	54819216
741	54908100	54922921	54937744	54952569	54967396
742	55056400	55071241	55086084	55100929	55115776
743	55204900	55219761	55234624	55249489	55264356
744	55353600	55368481	55383364	55398249	55413136
745	55502500	55517401	55532304	55547209	55562116
746	55651600	55666521	55681444	55696369	55711296
747	55800900	55815841	55830784	55845729	55860676
748	55950400	55965361	55980324	55995289	56010256
749	56100100	56115081	56130064	56145049	56160036

5	6	7	8	9	n
49070025	49084036	49098049	49112064	49126081	700
49210225	49224256	49238289	49252324	49266361	701
49350625	49364676	49378729	49392784	49406841	702
49491225	49505296	49519369	49533444	49547521	703
49632025	49646116	49660209	49674304	49688401	704
49773025	49787136	49801249	49815364	49829481	705
49914225	49928356	49942489	49956624	49970761	706
50055625	50069776	50083929	50098084	50112241	707
50197225	50211396	50225569	50239744	50253921	708
50339025	50353216	50367409	50381604	50395801	709
50481025	50495236	50509449	50523664	50537881	710
50623225	50637456	50651689	50665924	50680161	711
50765625	50779876	50794129	50808384	50822641	712
50908225	50922496	50936769	50951044	50965321	713
51051025	51065316	51079609	51093904	51108201	714
51194025	51208336	51222649	51236964	51251281	715
51337225	51351556	51365889	51380224	51394561	716
51480625	51494976	51509329	51523684	51538041	717
51624225	51638596	51652969	51667344	51681721	718
51768025	51782416	51796809	51811204	51825601	719
51912025	51926436	51940849	51955264	51969681	720
52056225	52070656	52085089	52099524	52113961	721
52200625	52215076	52229529	52243984	52258441	722
52345225	52359696	52374169	52388644	52403121	723
52490025	52504516	52519009	52533504	52548001	724
52635025	52649536	52664049	52678564	52693081	725
52780225	52794756	52809289	52823824	52838361	726
52925625	52940176	52954729	52969284	52983841	727
53071225	53085796	53100369	53114944	53129521	728
53217025	53231616	53246209	53260804	53275401	729
53363025	53377636	53392249	53406864	53421481	730
53509225	53523856	53538489	53553124	53567761	731
53655625	53670276	53684929	53699584	53714241	732
53802225	53816896	53831569	53846244	53860921	733
53949025	53963716	53978409	53993104	54007801	734
54095025	54110736	54125449	54140164	54154881	735
54243225	54257956	54272689	54287424	54302161	736
54390625	54405376	54420129	54434884	54449641	737
54538225	54552996	54567769	54582544	54597321	738
54686025	54700816	54715609	54730404	54745201	739
54834025	54848836	54863649	54878464	54893281	740
54982225	54997056	55011889	55026724	55041561	741
55130625	55145476	55160329	55175184	55190041	742
55279225	55294096	55308969	55323844	55338721	743
55428025	55442916	55457809	55472704	55487601	744
55577025	55591936	55606849	55621764	55636681	745
55726225	55741156	55756089	55771024	55785961	746
55875625	55890576	55905529	55920484	55935441	747
56025225	56040196	56055169	56070144	56085121	748
56175025	56190016	56205009	56220004	56235001	749

n	0	1	2	3	4
750	56250000	56265001	56280004	56295009	56310016
751	56400100	56415121	56430144	56445169	56460196
752	56550400	56565441	56580484	56595529	56610576
753	56700900	56715961	56731024	56746089	56761156
754	56851600	56866681	56881764	56896849	56911936
755	57002500	57017601	57032704	57047809	57062916
756	57153600	57168721	57183844	57198969	57214096
757	57304900	57320041	57335184	57350329	57365476
758	57456400	57471561	57486724	57501889	57517056
759	57608100	57623281	57638464	57653649	57668836
760	57760000	57775201	57790404	57805609	57820816
761	57912100	57927321	57942544	57957769	57972996
762	58064400	58079641	58094884	58110129	58125376
763	58216900	58232161	58247424	58262689	58277956
764	58369600	58384881	58400164	58415449	58430736
765	58522500	58537801	58553104	58568409	58583716
766	58675600	58690921	58706244	58721569	58736896
767	58828900	58844241	58859584	58874929	58890276
768	58982400	58997761	59013124	59028489	59043856
769	59136100	59151481	59166864	59182249	59197636
770	59290000	59305401	59320804	59336209	59351616
771	59444100	59459521	59474944	59490369	59505796
772	59598400	59613841	59629284	59644729	59660176
773	59752900	59768361	59783824	59799289	59814756
774	59907600	59923081	59938564	59954049	59969536
775	60062500	60078001	60093504	60109009	60124516
776	60217600	60233121	60248644	60264169	60279696
777	60372900	60388441	60403984	60419529	60435076
778	60528400	60543961	60559524	60575089	60590656
779	60684100	60699681	60715264	60730849	60746436
780	60840000	60855601	60871204	60886809	60902416
781	60996100	61011721	61027344	61042969	61058596
782	61152400	61168041	61183684	61199329	61214976
783	61308900	61324561	61340224	61355889	61371556
784	61465600	61481281	61496964	61512649	61528336
785	61622500	61638201	61653904	61669609	61685316
786	61779600	61795321	61811044	61826769	61842496
787	61936900	61952641	61968384	61984129	61999876
788	62094400	62110161	62125924	62141689	62157456
789	62252100	62267881	62283664	62299449	62315236
790	62410000	62425801	62441604	62457409	62473216
791	62568100	62583921	62599744	62615569	62631396
792	62726400	62742241	62758084	62773929	62789776
793	62884900	62900761	62916624	62932489	62948356
794	63043600	63059481	63075364	63091249	63107136
795	63202500	63218401	63234304	63250209	63266116
796	63361600	63377521	63393444	63409369	63425296
797	63520900	63536841	63552784	63568729	63584676
798	63680400	63696361	63712324	63728289	63744256
799	63840100	63856081	63872064	63888049	63904036

5	6	7	8	9	n
56325025	56340036	56355049	56370064	56385081	750
56475225	56490256	56505289	56520324	56535361	751
56625625	56640676	56655729	56670784	56685841	752
56776225	56791296	56806369	56821444	56836521	753
56927025	56942116	56957209	56972304	56987401	754
57078025	57093136	57108249	57123364	57138481	755
57229225	57244356	57259489	57274624	57289761	756
57380625	57395776	57410929	57426084	57441241	757
57532225	57547396	57562569	57577744	57592921	758
57684025	57699216	57714409	57729604	57744801	759
57836025	57851236	57866449	57881664	57896881	760
57988225	58003456	58018689	58033924	58049161	761
58140625	58155876	58171129	58186384	58201641	762
58293225	58308496	58323769	58339044	58354321	763
58446025	58461316	58476609	58491904	58507201	764
58599025	58614336	58629649	58644964	58660281	765
58752225	58767556	58782889	58798224	58813561	766
58905625	58920976	58936329	58951684	58967041	767
59059225	59074596	59089969	59105344	59120721	768
59213025	59228416	59243809	59259204	59274601	769
59367025	59382436	59397849	59413264	59428681	770
59521225	59536656	59552089	59567524	59582961	771
59675625	59691076	59706529	59721984	59737441	772
59830225	59845696	59861169	59876644	59892121	773
59985025	60000516	60016009	60031504	60047001	774
60140025	60155536	60171049	60186564	60202081	775
60295225	60310756	60326289	60341824	60357361	776
60450625	60466176	60481729	60497284	60512841	777
60606225	60621796	60637369	60652944	60668521	778
60762025	60777616	60793209	60808804	60824401	779
60918025	60933636	60949249	60964864	60980481	780
61074225	61089856	61105489	61121124	61136761	781
61230625	61246276	61261929	61277584	61293241	782
61387225	61402896	61418569	61434244	61449921	783
61544025	61559716	61575409	61591104	61606801	784
61701025	61716736	61732449	61748164	61763881	785
61858225	61873956	61889689	61905424	61921161	786
62015625	62031376	62047129	62062884	62078641	787
62173225	62188996	62204769	62220544	62236321	788
62331025	62346816	62362609	62378404	62394201	789
62489025	62504836	62520649	62536464	62552281	790
62647225	62663056	62678889	62694724	62710561	791
62805625	62821476	62837329	62853184	62869041	792
62964225	62980096	62995969	63011844	63027721	793
63123025	63138916	63154809	63170704	63186601	794
63282025	63297936	63313849	63329764	63345681	795
63441225	63457156	63473089	63489024	63504961	796
63600625	63616576	63632529	63648484	63664441	797
63760225	63776196	63792169	63808144	63824121	798
63920025	63936016	63952009	63968004	63984001	799

n	0	1	2	3	4
800	64000000	64016001	64032004	64048009	64064016
801	64160100	64176121	64192144	64208169	64224196
802	64320400	64336441	64352484	64368529	64384576
803	64480900	64496961	64513024	64529089	64545156
804	64641600	64657681	64673764	64689849	64705936
805	64802500	64818601	64834704	64850809	64866916
806	64963600	64979721	64995844	65011969	65028096
807	65124900	65141041	65157184	65173329	65189476
808	65286400	65302561	65318724	65334889	65351056
809	65448100	65464281	65480464	65496649	65512836
810	65610000	65626201	65642404	65658609	65674816
811	65772100	65788321	65804544	65820769	65836996
812	65934400	65950641	65966884	65983129	65999376
813	66096900	66113161	66129424	66145689	66161956
814	66259600	66275881	66292164	66308449	66324736
815	66422500	66438801	66455104	66471409	66487716
816	66585600	66601921	66618244	66634569	66650896
817	66748900	66765241	66781584	66797929	66814276
818	66912400	66928761	66945124	66961489	66977856
819	67076100	67092481	67108864	67125249	67141636
820	67240000	67256401	67272804	67289209	67305616
821	67404100	67420521	67436944	67453369	67469796
822	67568400	67584841	67601284	67617729	67634176
823	67732900	67749361	67765824	67782289	67798756
824	67897600	67914081	67930564	67947049	67963536
825	68062500	68079001	68095504	68112009	68128516
826	68227600	68244121	68260644	68277169	68293696
827	68392900	68409441	68425984	68442529	68459076
828	68558400	68574961	68591524	68608089	68624656
829	68724100	68740681	68757264	68773849	68790436
830	68890000	68906601	68923204	68939809	68956416
831	69056100	69072721	69089344	69105969	69122596
832	69222400	69239041	69255684	69272329	69288976
833	69388900	69405561	69422224	69438889	69455556
834	69555600	69572281	69588964	69605649	69622336
835	69722500	69739201	69755904	69772609	69789316
836	69889600	69906321	69923044	69939769	69956496
837	70056900	70073641	70090384	70107129	70123876
838	70224400	70241161	70257924	70274689	70291456
839	70392100	70408881	70425664	70442449	70459236
840	70560000	70576801	70593604	70610409	70627216
841	70728100	70744921	70761744	70778569	70795396
842	70896400	70913241	70930084	70946929	70963776
843	71064900	71081761	71098624	71115489	71132356
844	71233600	71250481	71267364	71284249	71301136
845	71402500	71419401	71436304	71453209	71470116
846	71571600	71588521	71605444	71622369	71639296
847	71740900	71757841	71774784	71791729	71808676
848	71910400	71927361	71944324	71961289	71978256
849	72080100	72097081	72114064	72131049	72148036

5	6	7	8	9	n
64080025	64096036	64112049	64128064	64144081	800
64240225	64256256	64272289	64288324	64304361	801
64400625	64416676	64432729	64448784	64464841	802
64561225	64577296	64593369	64609444	64625521	803
64722025	64738116	64754209	64770304	64786401	804
64883025	64899136	64915249	64931364	64947481	805
65044225	65060356	65076489	65092624	65108761	806
65205625	65221776	65237929	65254084	65270241	807
65367225	65383396	65399569	65415744	65431921	808
65529025	65545216	65561409	65577604	65593801	809
65691025	65707236	65723449	65739664	65755881	810
65853225	65869456	65885689	65901924	65918161	811
66015625	66031876	66048129	66064384	66080641	812
66178225	66194496	66210769	66227044	66243321	813
66341025	66357316	66373609	66389904	66406201	814
66504025	66520336	66536649	66552964	66569281	815
66667225	66683556	66699889	66716224	66732561	816
66830625	66846976	66863329	66879684	66896041	817
66994225	67010596	67026969	67043344	67059721	818
67158025	67174416	67190809	67207204	67223601	819
67322025	67338436	67354849	67371264	67387681	820
67486225	67502656	67519089	67535524	67551961	821
67650625	67667076	67683529	67699984	67716441	822
67815225	67831696	67848169	67864644	67881121	823
67980025	67996516	68013009	68029504	68046001	824
68145025	68161536	68178049	68194564	68211081	825
68310225	68326756	68343289	68359824	68376361	826
68475625	68492176	68508729	68525284	68541841	827
68641225	68657796	68674369	68690944	68707521	828
68807025	68823616	68840209	68856804	68873401	829
68973025	68989636	69006249	69022864	69039481	830
69139225	69155856	69172489	69189124	69205761	831
69305625	69322276	69338929	69355584	69372241	832
69472225	69488896	69505569	69522244	69538921	833
69639025	69655716	69672409	69689104	69705801	834
69806025	69822736	69839449	69856164	69872881	835
69973225	69989956	70006689	70023424	70040161	836
70140625	70157376	70174129	70190884	70207641	837
70308225	70324996	70341769	70358544	70375321	838
70476025	70492816	70509609	70526404	70543201	839
70644025	70660836	70677649	70694464	70711281	840
70812225	70829056	70845889	70862724	70879561	841
70980625	70997476	71014329	71031184	71048041	842
71149225	71166096	71182969	71199844	71216721	843
71318025	71334916	71351809	71368704	71385601	844
71487025	71503936	71520849	71537764	71554681	845
71656225	71673156	71690089	71707024	71723961	846
71825625	71842576	71859529	71876484	71893441	847
71995225	72012196	72029169	72046144	72063121	848
72165025	72182016	72199009	72216004	72233001	849

n	0	1	2	3	4
850	72250000	72267001	72284004	72301009	72318016
851	72420100	72437121	72454144	72471169	72488196
852	72590400	72607441	72624484	72641529	72658576
853	72760900	72777961	72795024	72812089	72829156
854	72931600	72948681	72965764	72982849	72999936
855	73102500	73119601	73136704	73153809	73170916
856	73273600	73290721	73307844	73324969	73342096
857	73444900	73462041	73479184	73496329	73513476
858	73616400	73633561	73650724	73667889	73685056
859	73788100	73805281	73822464	73839649	73856836
860	73960000	73977201	73994404	74011609	74028816
861	74132100	74149321	74166544	74183769	74200996
862	74304400	74321641	74338884	74356129	74373376
863	74476900	74494161	74511424	74528689	74545956
864	74649600	74666881	74684164	74701449	74718736
865	74822500	74839801	74857104	74874409	74891716
866	74995600	75012921	75030244	75047569	75064896
867	75168900	75186241	75203584	75220929	75238276
868	75342400	75359761	75377124	75394489	75411856
869	75516100	75533481	75550864	75568249	75585636
870	75690000	75707401	75724804	75742209	75759616
871	75864100	75881521	75898944	75916369	75933796
872	76038400	76055841	76073284	76090729	76108176
873	76212900	76230361	76247824	76265289	76282756
874	76387600	76405081	76422564	76440049	76457536
875	76562500	76580001	76597504	76615009	76632516
876	76737600	76755121	76772644	76790169	76807696
877	76912900	76930441	76947984	76965529	76983076
878	77088400	77105961	77123524	77141089	77158656
879	77264100	77281681	77299264	77316849	77334436
880	77440000	77457601	77475204	77492809	77510416
881	77616100	77633721	77651344	77668969	77686596
882	77792400	77810041	77827684	77845329	77862976
883	77968900	77986561	78004224	78021889	78039556
884	78145600	78163281	78180964	78198649	78216336
885	78322500	78340201	78357904	78375609	78393316
886	78499600	78517321	78535044	78552769	78570496
887	78676900	78694641	78712384	78730129	78747876
888	78854400	78872161	78889924	78907689	78925456
889	79032100	79049881	79067664	79085449	79103236
890	79210000	79227801	79245604	79263409	79281216
891	79388100	79405921	79423744	79441569	79459396
892	79566400	79584241	79602084	79619929	79637776
893	79744900	79762761	79780624	79798489	79816356
894	79923600	79941481	79959364	79977249	79995136
895	80102500	80120401	80138304	80156209	80174116
896	80281600	80299521	80317444	80335369	80353296
897	80460900	80478841	80496784	80514729	80532676
898	80640400	80658361	80676324	80694289	80712256
899	80820100	80838081	80856064	80874049	80892036

5	6	7	8	9	n
72335025	72352036	72369049	72386064	72403081	850
72505225	72522256	72539289	72556324	72573361	851
72675625	72692676	72709729	72726784	72743841	852
72846225	72863296	72880369	72897444	72914521	853
73017025	73034116	73051209	73068304	73085401	854
73188025	73205136	73222249	73239364	73256481	855
73359225	73376356	73393489	73410624	73427761	856
73530625	73547776	73564929	73582084	73599241	857
73702225	73719396	73736569	73753744	73770921	858
73874025	73891216	73908409	73925604	73942801	859
74046025	74063236	74080449	74097664	74114881	860
74218225	74235456	74252689	74269924	74287161	861
74390625	74407876	74425129	74442384	74459641	862
74563225	74580496	74597769	74615044	74632321	863
74736025	74753316	74770609	74787904	74805201	864
74909025	74926336	74943649	74960964	74978281	865
75082225	75099556	75116889	75134224	75151561	866
75255625	75272976	75290329	75307684	75325041	867
75429225	75446596	75463969	75481344	75498721	868
75603025	75620416	75637809	75655204	75672601	869
75777025	75794436	75811849	75829264	75846681	870
75951225	75968656	75986089	76003524	76020961	871
76125625	76143076	76160529	76177984	76195441	872
76300225	76317696	76335169	76352644	76370121	873
76475025	76492516	76510009	76527504	76545001	874
76650025	76667536	76685049	76702564	76720081	875
76825225	76842756	76860289	76877824	76895361	876
77000625	77018176	77035729	77053284	77070841	877
77176225	77193796	77211369	77228944	77246521	878
77352025	77369616	77387209	77404804	77422401	879
77528025	77545636	77563249	77580864	77598481	880
77704225	77721856	77739489	77757124	77774761	881
77880625	77898276	77915929	77933584	77951241	882
78057225	78074896	78092569	78110244	78127921	883
78234025	78251716	78269409	78287104	78304801	884
78411025	78428736	78446449	78464164	78481881	885
78588225	78605956	78623689	78641424	78659161	886
78765625	78783376	78801129	78818884	78836641	887
78943225	78960996	78978769	78996544	79014321	888
79121025	79138816	79156609	79174404	79192201	889
79299025	79316836	79334649	79352464	79370281	890
79477225	79495056	79512889	79530724	79548561	891
79655625	79673476	79691329	79709184	79727041	892
79834225	79852096	79869969	79887844	79905721	893
80013025	80030916	80048809	80066704	80084601	894
80192025	80209936	80227849	80245764	80263681	895
80371225	80389156	80407089	80425024	80442961	896
80550625	80568576	80586529	80604484	80622441	897
80730225	80748196	80766169	80784144	80802121	898
80910025	80928016	80946009	80964004	80982001	899

n	0	1	2	3	4
900	81000000	81018001	81036004	81054009	81072016
901	81180100	81198121	81216144	81234169	81252196
902	81360400	81378441	81396484	81414529	81432576
903	81540900	81558961	81577024	81595089	81613156
904	81721600	81739681	81757764	81775849	81793936
905	81902500	81920601	81938704	81956809	81974916
906	82083600	82101721	82119844	82137969	82156096
907	82264900	82283041	82301184	82319329	82337476
908	82446400	82464561	82482724	82500889	82519056
909	82628100	82646281	82664464	82682649	82700836
910	82810000	82828201	82846404	82864609	82882816
911	82992100	83010321	83028544	83046769	83064996
912	83174400	83192641	83210884	83229129	83247376
913	83356900	83375161	83393424	83411689	83429956
914	83539600	83557881	83576164	83594449	83612736
915	83722500	83740801	83759104	83777409	83795716
916	83905600	83923921	83942244	83960569	83978896
917	84088900	84107241	84125584	84143929	84162276
918	84272400	84290761	84309124	84327489	84345856
919	84456100	84474481	84492864	84511249	84529636
920	84640000	84658401	84676804	84695209	84713616
921	84824100	84842521	84860944	84879369	84897796
922	85008400	85026841	85045284	85063729	85082176
923	85192900	85211361	85229824	85248289	85266756
924	85377600	85396081	85414564	85433049	85451536
925	85562500	85581001	85599504	85618009	85636516
926	85747600	85766121	85784644	85803169	85821696
927	85932900	85951441	85969984	85988529	86007076
928	86118400	86136961	86155524	86174089	86192656
929	86304100	86322681	86341264	86359849	86378436
930	86490000	86508601	86527204	86545809	86564416
931	86676100	86694721	86713344	86731969	86750596
932	86862400	86881041	86899684	86918329	86936976
933	87048900	87067561	87086224	87104889	87123556
934	87235600	87254281	87272964	87291649	87310336
935	87422500	87441201	87459904	87478609	87497316
936	87609600	87628321	87647044	87665769	87684496
937	87796900	87815641	87834384	87853129	87871876
938	87984400	88003161	88021924	88040689	88059456
939	88172100	88190881	88209664	88228449	88247236
940	88360000	88378801	88397604	88416409	88435216
941	88548100	88566921	88585744	88604569	88623396
942	88736400	88755241	88774084	88792929	88811776
943	88924900	88943761	88962624	88981489	89000356
944	89113600	89132481	89151364	89170249	89189136
945	89302500	89321401	89340304	89359209	89378116
946	89491600	89510521	89529444	89548369	89567296
947	89680900	89699841	89718784	89737729	89756676
948	89870400	89889361	89908324	89927289	89946256
949	90060100	90079081	90098064	90117049	90136036

5	.6	7	8	9	n
81090025	81108036	81126049	81144064	81162081	900
81270225	81288256	81306289	81324324	81342361	901
81450625	81468676	81486729	81504784	81522841	902
81631225	81649296	81667369	81685444	81703521	903
81812025	81830116	81848209	81866304	81884401	904
81993025	82011136	82029249	82047364	82065481	905
82174225	82192356	82210489	82228624	82246761	906
82355625	82373776	82391929	82410084	82428241	907
82537225	82555396	82573569	82591744	82609921	908
82719025	82737216	82755409	82773604	82791801	909
82901025	82919236	82937449	82955664	82973881	910
83083225	83101456	83119689	83137924	83156161	911
83265625	83283876	83302129	83320384	83338641	912
83448225	83466496	83484769	83503044	83521321	913
83631025	83649316	83667609	83685904	83704201	914
83814025	83832336	83850649	83868964	83887281	915
83997225	84015556	84033889	84052224	84070561	916
84180625	84198976	84217329	84235684	84254041	917
84364225	84382596	84400969	84419344	84437721	918
84548025	84566416	84584809	84603204	84621601	919
84732025	84750436	84768849	84787264	84805681	920
84916225	84934656	84953089	84971524	84989961	921
85100625	85119076	85137529	85155984	85174441	922
85285225	85303696	85322169	85340644	85359121	923
85470025	85488516	85507009	85525504	85544001	924
85655025	85673536	85692049	85710564	85729081	925
85840225	85858756	85877289	85895824	85914361	926
86025625	86044176	86062729	86081284	86099841	927
86211225	86229796	86248369	86266944	86285521	928
86397025	86415616	86434209	86452804	86471401	929
86583025	86601636	86620249	86638864	86657481	930
86769225	86787856	86806489	86825124	86843761	931
86955625	86974276	86992929	87011584	87030241	932
87142225	87160896	87179569	87198244	87216921	933
87329025	87347716	87366409	87385104	87403801	934
87516025	87534736	87553449	87572164	87590881	935
87703225	87721956	87740689	87759424	87778161	936
87890625	87909376	87928129	87946884	87965641	937
88078225	88096996	88115769	88134544	88153321	938
88266025	88284816	88303609	88322404	88341201	939
88454025	88472836	88491649	88510464	88529281	940
88642225	88661056	88679889	88698724	88717561	941
88830625	88849476	88868329	88887184	88906041	942
89019225	89038096	89056969	89075844	89094721	943
89208025	89226916	89245809	89264704	89283601	944
89397025	89415936	89434849	89453764	89472681	945
89586225	89605156	89624089	89643024	89661961	946
89775625	89794576	89813529	89832484	89851441	947
89965225	89984196	90003169	90022144	90041121	948
90155025	90174016	90193009	90212004	90231001	949

n	0	1	2	3	4
950	90250000	90269001	90288004	90307009	90326016
951	90440100	90459121	90478144	90497169	90516196
952	90630400	90649441	90668484	90687529	90706576
953	90820900	90839961	90859024	90878089	90897156
954	91011600	91030681	91049764	91068849	91087936
955	91202500	91221601	91240704	91259809	91278916
956	91393600	91412721	91431844	91450969	91470096
957	91584900	91604041	91623184	91642329	91661476
958	91776400	91795561	91814724	91833889	91853056
959	91968100	91987281	92006464	92025649	92044836
960	92160000	92179201	92198404	92217609	92236816
961	92352100	92371321	92390544	92409769	92428996
962	92544400	92563641	92582884	92602129	92621376
963	92736900	92756161	92775424	92794689	92813956
964	92929600	92948881	92968164	92987449	93006736
965	93122500	93141801	93161104	93180409	93199716
966	93315600	93334921	93354244	93373569	93392896
967	93508900	93528241	93547584	93566929	93586276
968	93702400	93721761	93741124	93760489	93779856
969	93896100	93915481	93934864	93954249	93973636
970	94090000	94109401	94128804	94148209	94167616
971	94284100	94303521	94322944	94342369	94361796
972	94478400	94497841	94517284	94536729	94556176
973	94672900	94692361	94711824	94731289	94750756
974	94867600	94887081	94906564	94926049	94945536
975	95062500	95082001	95101504	95121009	95140516
976	95257600	95277121	95296644	95316169	95335696
977	95452900	95472441	95491984	95511529	95531076
978	95648400	95667961	95687524	95707089	95726656
979	95844100	95863681	95883264	95902849	95922436
980	96040000	96059601	96079204	96098809	96118416
981	96236100	96255721	96275344	96294969	96314596
982	96432400	96452041	96471684	96491329	96510976
983	96628900	96648561	96668224	96687889	96707556
984	96825600	96845281	96864964	96884649	96904336
985	97022500	97042201	97061904	97081609	97101316
986	97219600	97239321	97259044	97278769	97298496
987	97416900	97436641	97456384	97476129	97495876
988	97614400	97634161	97653924	97673689	97693456
989	97812100	97831881	97851664	97871449	97891236
990	98010000	98029801	98049604	98069409	98089216
991	98208100	98227921	98247744	98267569	98287396
992	98406400	98426241	98446084	98465929	98485776
993	98604900	98624761	98644624	98664489	98684356
994	98803600	98823481	98843364	98863249	98883136
995	99002500	99022401	99042304	99062209	99082116
996	99201600	99221521	99241444	99261369	99281296
997	99400900	99420841	99440784	99460729	99480676
998	99600400	99620361	99640324	99660289	99680256
999	99800100	99820081	99840064	99860049	99880036

5	6	7	8	9	n
90345025	90364036	90383049	90402064	90421081	950
90535225	90554256	90573289	90592324	90611361	951
90725625	90744676	90763729	90782784	90801841	952
90916225	90935296	90954369	90973444	90992521	953
91107025	91126116	91145209	91164304	91183401	954
91298025	91317136	91336249	91355364	91374481	955
91489225	91508356	91527489	91546624	91565761	956
91680625	91699776	91718929	91738084	91757241	957
91872225	91891396	91910569	91929744	91948921	958
92064025	92083216	92102409	92121604	92140801	959
92256025	92275236	92294449	92313664	92332881	960
92448225	92467456	92486689	92505924	92525161	961
92640625	92659876	92679129	92698384	92717641	962
92833225	92852496	92871769	92891044	92910321	963
93026025	93045316	93064609	93083904	93103201	964
93219025	93238336	93257649	93276964	93296281	965
93412225	93431556	93450889	93470224	93489561	966
93605625	93624976	93644329	93663684	93683041	967
93799225	93818596	93837969	93857344	93876721	968
93993025	94012416	94031809	94051204	94070601	969
94187025	94206436	94225849	94245264	94264681	970
94381225	94400656	94420089	94439524	94458961	971
94575625	94595076	94614529	94633984	94653441	972
94770225	94789696	94809169	94828644	94848121	973
94965025	94984516	95004009	95023504	95043001	974
95160025	95179536	95199049	95218564	95238081	975
95355225	95374756	95394289	95413824	95433361	976
95550625	95570176	95589729	95609284	95628841	977
95746225	95765796	95785369	95804944	95824521	978
95942025	95961616	95981209	96000804	96020401	979
96138025	96157636	96177249	96196864	96216481	980
96334225	96353856	96373489	96393124	96412761	981
96530625	96550276	96569929	96589584	96609241	982
96727225	96746896	96766569	96786244	96805921	983
96924025	96943716	96963409	96983104	97002801	984
97121025	97140736	97160449	97180164	97199881	985
97318225	97337956	97357689	97377424	97397161	986
97515625	97535376	97555129	97574884	97594641	987
97713225	97732996	97752769	97772544	97792321	988
97911025	97930816	97950609	97970404	97990201	989
98109025	98128836	98148649	98168464	98188281	990
98307225	98327056	98346889	98366724	98386561	991
98505625	98525476	98545329	98565184	98585041	992
98704225	98724096	98743969	98763844	98783721	993
98903025	98922916	98942809	98962704	98982601	994
99102025	99121936	99141849	99161764	99181681	995
99301225	99321156	99341089	99361024	99380961	996
99500625	99520576	99540529	99560484	99580441	997
99700225	99720196	99740169	99760144	99780121	998
99900025	99920016	99940009	99960004	99980001	999

Index

145